Conferring with Young Mathematicians at Work

Making Moments Matter

Catherine Twomey Fosnot

New Perspectives on Learning, LLC
1194 Ocean Avenue
New London, CT 06320

ISBN: 0997688602
ISBN-13: 978-0997688603

DEDICATION

This book is dedicated to my grandchildren: Josie, Cole, Maia, and Harrison

THIS BOOK INCLUDES SEVERAL VIDEO CLIPS OF THE AUTHOR AND EXEMPLARY TEACHERS CONFERRING WITH CHILDREN DURING MATH WORKSHOP. CLIPS ARE ALSO INCLUDED OF THE AUTHOR EXPLAINING SEVERAL LANDSCAPES OF LEARNING. ALL ARE PROVIDED COURTESY OF NEW PERSPECTIVES ONLINE, LLC.

THE VIDEO CLIPS ARE ACCESSIBLE VIA BOTH QR SCAN CODES AND WEB LINKS. APPS TO SCAN THE PROVIDED QR CODES CAN BE DOWNLOADED AT **WWW.SCAN.ME.** APPS FOR *IOS, ANDROID, AND WINDOWS,* FOR INSTANCE, ARE AVAILABLE ON THAT WEBSITE

.

CONTENTS

Acknowledgements

This book has been a long time in the making. It is the culmination of the many years I have spent in classrooms working with children and their teachers, both while directing Mathematics in the City and then over the last 8 years as President and CEO of New Perspectives on Learning.

Over these years, I have been lucky to have had many wonderful colleagues. As Steen (1990) says, "We build our ideas on the shoulders of giants." Ideas are generated in a community, and through history—not alone. I owe a debt of gratitude to so many, that if I begin naming them the list will be longer than the book. Most know who they are, and over the years in many of my previous books I have thanked them publicly.

In this book I want to give particular thanks to Maarten Dolk, who loves to joke with me that when we started working together my hair was blonde (it's now completely white), and he had hair (he now has none). Our very long collaboration has been a fruitful one: from our many days of Math in the City, to collaborating on the writing of the first three *Young Mathematicians at Work* books, to the development of our first multi-media project to document the vibrant math communities we were developing, to co-writing some of the *CFLM* units, to our more recent partnering to produce P2S2: a personalized professional support system.™ **www.NewPerspectivesOnline.net.** He also helped with the filming, editing, and crafting of the Vimeo clips that accompany this book, as well as the planning of the Quick Scans to access them within. I treasure every moment of our work together, but also the deep personal friendship that has developed through the years as a result.

Chapter 9 could not have been written without the help of Melissa and Bryan Becerra who have worked with me over the last year in the development of our assessment app: **www.NewPerspectivesOnAssessment.com.** Being able to confer without the distractions of taking notes is critical, and it was Melissa's idea to develop an app that would allow teachers to document learning digitally, in the moment as they confer, so they could focus on the children they are conferring with instead of on notetaking to more capably make the short moments we have when conferring matter. And then, Bryan, genius that he is, developed it. I am extremely grateful for all of their work on development, as well as their continuing work in helping teachers use the app well.

I also want to thank all of the current staff who work with me at New Perspectives On Learning, LLC who bring passion and excitement about mathematics to the many teachers and children we work with around the world. Each is listed on the website: **www.NewPerspectivesOnLearning.com.** A very special thanks goes to Janan Hamm who has done the largest amount of work, not only working in schools, but writing crosswalks for CFLM and several core curricula, working with Maarten and me on P2S2: monitoring the Forum and helping us field test aspects of the online platform.

Over the last 5 years we have been producing more CFLM units, and now have units out on geometry and measurement, as well as our earlier units on number and operation. I am grateful also to the many teachers who have worked with me on these, field testing in their classrooms, and writing up the units for other teachers to use. In particular, I want to thank Sylvia Glassco who has been doing much of the editing and graphics, as well.

Pat Luce and Meg Ceccarelli, my event planners, have taken over the advertising, registration, and invoicing for my workshops around the country and the Seminars by the Sea in New London, CT at Ocean Beach. Without the two of them, I would not be able to do what I do. They have removed a huge burden from my shoulders and given me the gift of time.

Last, but not least, a very special thanks to Randall Perry for giving me undisturbed time and a quiet secluded place in Malta to think and write.

Credits:
Figures 9.3-9.5 of the Landscapes of Learning are from Fosnot, C.T. ()2007. *Contexts for Learning Mathematics*. Portsmouth. NH: Heinemann Firsthand. Reprinted by permission of the publisher.

Figure 8.3 is a modification of a previous version published in Imm, Fosnot, Dolk, Jacob and Stylianou (2012*). Learning to Support Young Mathematicians at Work*. Portsmouth. NH: Heinemann. Modified by permission of the publisher.

The photography on pages 4, 54, and 76 is by Herbert Seignoret.
The photography on page 102 is by Mark Russell.
All other photography and video are provided by www.NewPerspectivesOnline.net.

Chapter One

* * *

What do I Ask?

"Each time one prematurely teaches a child something he could have discovered himself, that child is kept from inventing it and consequently from understanding it completely."

— Jean Piaget 1970, p. 715

Introduction

Questioning has become one of the biggest challenges of teachers everywhere as they rise to the challenge of transforming their classrooms into communities of mathematicians. The CCSS Standards of Mathematical Practice require that children engage in problem solving with tenacity and confidence, use models as tools for thinking, and read and write viable arguments. This mandate demands that teachers foster a climate conducive to the generating of mathematics rather than the explanation of it. Teachers have been told that they have a new role—one of a facilitator, rather than an explainer.

As I traverse the country doing workshops, a chorus of requests for workshops on questioning greets me. "I know I shouldn't tell them what to do," teachers say to me, "but what do I ask?" Many administrators request, "Help my teachers learn to question better during math workshop. They don't know what to ask." When I am in classrooms, I see teachers over and over again just asking general questions like, "What did you do to solve the problem? How did you start? What did you do next? Why did you decide to do that?" The conferral then invariably ends with something like, "You're not done yet though. Put in words, pictures or symbols for me what you did. Remember, you have to explain your thinking."

It's not that these are bad questions. Certainly they might cause children to reflect as they respond, and reflection is most often a good thing. The problem is just that they aren't powerful enough to really be transformative—to really *ensure* growth and development in mathematics. They aren't characteristic of mentoring, and good math teachers are not just facilitators of learning; we are mentors. Our task is to see the young learners in our care as our apprentices and welcome and initiate them into the community of praxis of the discipline —into the *generating* of mathematics. And, part of the generating of mathematics is to write viable arguments, which should not be confused with the directive, "Explain your thinking." Mathematicians don't just tell what they did; they build a defense of their results. They examine structure and regularity, put forth conjectures, and craft proofs.

Let's go into a classroom and witness firsthand the struggles and challenges of new and veteran teachers alike, as they transform their roles and attempt to implement vibrant math workshops.

In the Classroom: a conferral

Eileen, a veteran teacher of 30 years, is not new to math workshop. Her school began the transformation to an inquiry model over ten years ago with an initial focus on writing. Back then, she had easily transformed her writing instruction from one characterized by direct instruction, essay assignments for practice, and feedback with a red pen, to the running of powerful writing workshops. She now enjoys moving around the room and conferring with her engaged third graders as they attempt to craft leads to hook an audience, to develop characters, and to tell stories from their imaginations. Each year she revels in the growth and development she witnesses as her children blossom over the course of a year into capable writers.

Four years ago, her district had begun a similar math initiative. Over the last couple of years, Eileen attended several professional development workshops at a nearby university on the use of problems to generate mathematics, on questioning, and on the use of manipulatives. Yet, it still remains a puzzle to her why she finds it so difficult to question during math workshop, particularly when it feels so natural to her now during writing workshop. She knows she should let her children solve problems in their own ways, but they often make mistakes and sometimes don't even know how to start. They beg her to tell them what to do, and even when they do have a way to start, they seem to use the same inefficient strategies, over and over.

Eileen feels stymied. "If I don't tell them what to do," she wonders, "how will they ever develop better strategies?" Yesterday, in fact, she had been conferring with two of her third graders, Scarlett and Cassandra, as they worked to solve a grocery store problem about the cost of 6 pounds of carrots at $.89 per pound. The conferral had ended with tears and an outburst from Scarlett, "I hate math!" Eileen thinks to herself, to be honest I'm beginning to feel the same way—tired of trying not to tell them what to do, and I'm frustrated because I don't know what to ask! She tries to shrug off these feelings and commits herself to having a better conferral with the girls today.

As she sits to confer, she notes the girls are busily chatting about what they have on their paper. [Their work is shown in Figure 1.1.] Today they are working on determining how long to cook a 24 lb. turkey, at 15 minutes per pound. Determined to be encouraging today, she opens the conferral by using a lead question she often uses in writing workshop—one recommended by Carl Anderson in his book on conferring with young writers. "So how is it going today?" Eileen begins, warmly and with a special look to Scarlett.

Scarlett shrugs, "We're actually done. Can we make a poster now?" Eileen notes that Scarlett has positioned herself next to Cassandra, and it is Cassandra who holds the pencil and appears to be the one doing the work. She also notes that the girls have a wrong answer.

"So tell me what you did," Eileen smiles, trying to sound interested and encouraging. She specifically targets her question at Scarlett to see what she understands of the work that Cassandra has apparently done.

"We wrote it right over here because you always tell us we have to explain our thinking," Scarlett points to the right side of the paper and begins reading what they have written, "We know $50 + 50 = 100$ and 60 is 10 more." To get her to reflect on the apparent error Eileen stops her from continuing, and asks, "Where did the 100 come from?"

"I just told you," Scarlett huffs impatiently, "from $50 + 50$."

"Right. So where did the fifties come from?" Eileen presses on, hoping that if she continues getting the girls to explain what they did, she might eventually get them to correct their mistake.

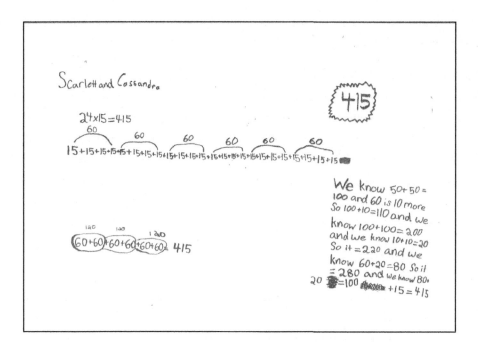

Figure 1.1
Scarlett and Cassandra's Work

Nonplussed, Scarlett retorts, "From the sixties, like I said."

"Okay, I see that, so from this 60 you got 50, and from this other one you also got 50, and then you added 10. Where did that come from?"

"From the 60."

"And did this 60 have a 10, too?"

Scarlett now looks puzzled and calls on Cassandra to help. "I think it is down here where it says 10 + 10 = 20. Is that right, Cassandra?"

"Yep, that's right." Cassandra confirms what Scarlet has just said with a proud grin, oblivious to the fact that Eileen is asking about the second 60, not the third and fourth.

Eileen is now wondering where to go next with her questioning. The line of questioning she has been taking seems to be getting her nowhere and she knows it will take time to get the girls to explain each step. She reads again what the girls have written and although she knows their answer is wrong, she is challenged to understand what they have done to get it and how to get them to fix their mistake. And, other children in her class are now beckoning her. She has a big class this year of 30 and she can't spend all of her time with just these two girls. She decides it might be wise to let the girls rethink themselves what they did, and so she leaves them with an assignment, "What I want you to do is to write down underneath each 60 the numbers you used so you can check your work. Show me where the numbers are coming from—how you are breaking them up. I don't think your answer is right and I want you to figure out where you made your mistake."

"What is the real answer then?" Scarlett looks at her imploringly.

Not wanting to tell something they could discover for themselves, Eileen leaves them with, "You'll figure it out. You're on a good path."

As she leaves to confer with other children, she hears Scarlett mutter under her breath to Cassandra, "She always wants us to show our thinking. And, why won't she tell us the answer? I hate math."

"What had gone awry?" Eileen wonders. "Why do her conferrals in math workshop seem to go nowhere when it seems so easy and natural in her writing workshop?"

Reflecting on the Challenges

As Eileen's struggle shows, the transference of strategies that work in writer's workshop to math workshop is not automatic. Although there are deep philosophical and pedagogical roots underneath the running of vibrant math and writing workshops, there are also some differences because of the nature of the disciplines. Good conferrals in writing demand a deep appreciation and understanding of the process of writing. The same is true of good conferrals in math—one needs to understand, deeply, the development of mathematics and the processes mathematicians use to make meaning.

As teachers, we will need to develop our ability to question well in math workshop in order to foster development because, as Piaget helps us to realize in his quote in the epigraph to this chapter, "Each time one prematurely teaches a child something he could have discovered himself, that child is kept from inventing it and consequently from understanding it completely."

Inventing and understanding are critical to the development of a positive growth mindset. For children to attack problems with tenacity and confidence, to use models as tools for thinking, and to read and write viable arguments competently, conferring in ways that ensure learner ownership of the mathematics is required. And, we need to make these moments matter. One of the reasons Eileen's conferral went awry is that it was focused on the product of the mathematics, rather than on the process of doing mathematics; it was focused on the solution of the problem, rather than the development of the mathematician.

In the next chapter we'll examine some similarities and differences between writing and math conferrals in more depth, and then in light of this information we'll rewind Eileen's conferral and explore how it might have gone differently.

Chapter Two

* * *

Conferring During Writing and Math Workshops:

Similarities and Differences

"The vast majority of us imagine ourselves as literature people or math people. But the truth is that the massive processor known as the human brain is neither a literature organ, nor a math organ. It is both and more."

— **John Green**
http://www.goodreads.com/quotes/tag/comparison

Some Similarities

Learning to confer well during writing workshop most often required teachers to immerse themselves first in the process of writing—*to see themselves as writers.* Deeply appreciating the writing process helped them to more capably mentor others, as it enabled them to come to understand that writers choose topics that personally matter and that an audience is critical to their process. Crafting powerful openings and endings, memorable lines, engaging plots, and complex, interesting and believable characters are all processes employed by competent writers to hook their audience and get them to engage with the text, and each develops over time. Writers work on pieces tenaciously, enjoying the revising and crafting because they feel they are creating an object of beauty. The act of writing is creative; writers, as they write, are making meaning for themselves. They are clarifying their ideas and bringing new thoughts to light. The writer, Donald Murray, once said about his process, "I write to surprise myself." And similarly the playwright, Alan Bennett, said, "I don't try to bring myself into my writing; I write to find myself."

Mathematics is no different. As they work on problems, mathematicians build meaning; they seek structure and regularity. They look for interesting relationships by substituting and exchanging equivalent expressions to simplify problems. They often use a variety of mathematical models to depict and examine relationships, as various models have different assets and limitations that can hinder or bring new relationships to light. They craft arguments—proofs—for an audience. The audience is as critical to the generative process as it is for the writer. In the end, the logic of the proof must bring other mathematicians to say upon reading it, "I'm convinced; it must be so."

The mathematician works on problems tenaciously and revises, edits, and polishes proofs until the story seems crisp and elegant. As Paul Lockhart says in his book *A Mathematician's Lament: How School Cheats Us out of Our Most Fascinating and Imaginative Art Form*, "It is the story that matters not just the ending."

* * *

I understand Lockhart's lament firsthand. Most of the courses I took in my preparation as an educator were designed more about endings. I would in fact term them, "math history courses" rather than courses in mathematics. Each had an apparent "box of content objectives" –a list of procedures, concepts, and formulae to be covered for tests and later application. My job as a learner was to study these endings—to come to understand what other past mathematicians through the years had generated and proven. With the exception of high school geometry, where I was finally asked to explore and actually construct my own proofs, I rarely was asked to generate or prove anything. My task as a learner was to study the end result of someone else's mathematics, to understand why the results were important, and to become proficient with their procedures so that I could use them at another time.

It's not that math history is a bad thing. Knowing what giants in the field before us have done and how and when those procedures can be applied to solve problems is helpful. As humans we all build our ideas on "the shoulders of giants" (Steen, 1990) no matter the discipline. Writers can learn a lot by studying what other writers before them have done. So can artists, musicians, and scientists. But imagine if a writer was only given opportunities to study the works of others for 20 years before ever trying to produce a piece of their own making!

For me, the real love of math came when I realized it was about building my own meaning. It was not only about solving someone else's problem; it was about inquiry—mathematizing the world around me, and then mathematizing the mathematics to make my solution crisper, more elegant.

I am sure I have learned more mathematics as I have worked on problems and inquiries with my students (pre- and in-service teachers), and the children in their classes, than I ever did in the many math classes I took. The twists and turns that inquiries would take, because someone in the community put forth a conjecture or an alternative strategy, caused us to wonder if the conjectures and strategies were generalizable and to work out proofs. The mathematics was generated in the community as we built our ideas on each other's and discussed a variety of solutions. We were no longer learning solely about someone else's ending; we were making our own stories.

When I sit down to confer with a developing mathematician, I have to constantly remind myself that my goal is to support the development of the young mathematician sitting next to me. It is not to fix the piece of mathematics. Lucy Calkins (1994) said something quite similar about writing conferrals: they need to be about developing a young writer, not red-penning the piece of writing.

First and foremost, a conferral with a child, whether it is during writing workshop or math workshop, is a conversation (Anderson, 2000). There is a flow to the conversation as the dialogue goes back and forth from student to teacher. If only one person is doing most of the talking it is not a conversation; it is a monologue. A teacher who spends the bulk of conferral time explaining to children what she thinks they should do is not having a conversation.

Reciprocally, there is not much of a conversation when children are spending all of the time explaining what they are doing, and the only response from the teacher is, "Why? What will you do next? Do you think that will work? Explain your thinking." Conferrals are opportunities to get to know *how* children are thinking, to converse about the strategies they are trying, and to offer them support and insights that might be helpful as they work to meet their goals—to write *their* mathematics stories.

Powerful conferrals have a certain structure. They usually begin with an invitation to the students to talk about what they are doing and/or the challenges they are having. As students explain, teachers listen intently with respect and genuine interest because knowing the learners' goals, ideas, and strategies will determine where the conferral goes next.

At a point during the conferral the focus shifts to what learners might try next; how they might craft their work tighter to become a better writer, or mathematician. In general, the conferral begins with a discussion of the learners' ideas and goals, a celebration of some of the interesting, important ideas inherent in the approach, and then an "upping of the ante" occurs—a challenge important to development of the young writer or mathematician is offered as a focus for further work. And right there is the rub: precisely because the disciplines of writing and mathematics differ, knowing where to go next with a developing writer isn't automatically transferrable to knowing where to go next with a developing mathematician.

Some Differences

To support the development of a mathematician we have to know something about what it really means to do mathematics, but we need to know more: we need to understand the development of the mathematical topic and strand we are conferring about. Conferring in a math workshop is not about introducing new skills and concepts from an a priori list of objectives; nor is it about helping learners get a correct answer to the problem at hand. It is about supporting the *development of a young mathematician* to become a better, more competent, mathematician.

Conferring during math workshop requires us to engage in the process of *doing* mathematics *with* our students—fostering enjoyment in the crafting of "the story," not just guiding our learners to a solution. Conferrals should foster excitement, puzzlement, confidence, and in general the development of a positive growth-mindset towards mathematics.

If you want to see a video of a good math conferral in action, go to
http://tiny.cc/NPO1

or scan the QR Scan Code provided here:

The video shows a third grade teacher, Carolyn Hammonds, from the Beauvoir Cathedral School in Washington D.C. conferring with two of her students as they work on an investigation in the CFLM unit, Muffles Truffles. The children are trying to determine how many boxes are needed for various types of truffles when the boxes each hold 10. During their investigation they begin to notice a pattern for division by 10.

The video is provided courtesy of **www.NewPerspectivesOnline.net.** *More video of conferrals as well as a full course on conferring taught by the author, for which this book can be a reader, is also available on the website.*

A Comparison of Writing and Mathematics Conferrals

	Conferrals with Writers	Conferrals with Mathematicians
Similarities	It's a conversation. It has a structure comprised first of listening and/or noting what the writers are doing and what their goals are, then celebrating some specifics of the ideas and strategies being tried and suggesting further things to try as a challenge. Its goal is not to fix the piece of writing but to support the development of a writer.	It's a conversation. It has a structure comprised first of listening and/or noting what the mathematicians are doing and what their goals are, then celebrating some specifics of the ideas and strategies being tried and suggesting further things to try as a challenge. Its goal is not to fix the piece of mathematics but to support the development of a mathematician.
Differences	The conferral shifts at a point with a challenge to support the development of the writer by offering feedback, suggestions, and a specific focus to work on such as: • Crafting leads and endings • Developing characters and conversation • Examining the main point of the story, the angle • Expanding "small moments" by adding detail and/or eliminating extraneous detail • Developing settings, painting mental images • Taking the audience into consideration • Examining word choice and playing with language • Working on a personal style	The conferral shifts at a point with a challenge to support the development of the mathematician by offering feedback, suggestions, and a specific focus to work on such as: • Examining structure and regularity (looking for patterns or interesting relationships, comparing the problem to other similar problems) • Finding ways to make the strategy more efficient • Examining the problem with different models as tools for thinking and noting insights • Treating expressions as equivalent objects that can be exchanged to simplify the problem and/or solution • Generalizing beyond the problem, for example generating big ideas, proposing conjectures, and working to prove them • Writing an argument—a proof to convince others

Back to the Classroom: A rerun of the conferral from Chapter One

The focus of Eileen's conferral in Chapter One was on helping the girls see and fix their error. To Eileen, the purpose of the conferral was to support the girls to get the correct answer to the problem. Could there have been a better focus—one that might have left them excited and empowered—one that would have resulted in a positive growth-mindset towards the *doing* of mathematics—one that would have been more conducive to the development of a mathematician? What might that look like?

Look again at the piece of work in Figure 1.1. Note that the girls started, as one might expect from third graders, with a repeated addition strategy. To make the addition easier though, they then regrouped the groups into groups of 60, and then later regrouped again into groups of 120. This regrouping of groups is a big advance from just repeated addition of 15s.

One might begin by discussing and celebrating how they thought to regroup to make the repeated addition more efficient, then shifting the focus to a discussion on the equivalence: $24 \times 15 = 6 \times 60 = 3 \times 120$, with mention given to how mathematicians love looking for equivalent pieces and simplifying their work with them. This focus might support Scarlett and Cassandra to invent doubling and halving as a powerful strategy for multiplication and to construct the underlying big idea of the associative property:

$$(6 \times 4) \times 15 = 6 \times (4 \times 15)$$

$$(3 \times 2) \times 60 = 3 \times (2 \times 60)$$

The conferral might then end with them considering how to write a convincing argument for the community. Ultimately, understanding and proving these relations, might support the development of exchanging an equivalent expression when multiplying. For example when solving 4.5×14, one could substitute 9×7, as these expressions are equivalent:

$$4.5 \times (2 \times 7) = (4.5 \times 2) \times 7$$

When strategies like these are used for computation, the arithmetic is simpler and there is much less of a chance of making computation errors. Further, developing computation strategies like these fosters eventual outcomes like multiplying efficiently using the properties of operations—one of the year end objectives of the Common Core State Standards. Let's try rerunning the conferral taking this tack and see what happens.

* * *

Eileen notes as she sits down with Scarlett and Cassandra that they have the wrong answer. She realizes, though, that if she focuses on developing their understanding of the operation and refining their strategy to become more efficient, they won't have as much arithmetic computation to do. In the long run, this will enable them to make fewer mistakes. It is all the tedious arithmetic that is causing their errors in the first place; they lose track of the many pieces they have done.

Of course answers matter, particularly on the standardized tests they will take in the spring, and right answers are important to mathematicians. To say correct answers don't matter would raise shackles on a mathematician. But, right now, getting the correct answer to this problem is not the issue at hand. This is not a final test; the problem is being used as a context to generate learning, not to test it. Eileen realizes there is a powerful learning moment right now not to be missed—a moment far more powerful than helping the girls to correct their answer. The answer will most likely be corrected later anyway when the girls post their work in the class gallery walk and note that other children have a different answer. They will likely re-examine their computation and fix the error, themselves. Right now, Eileen wants to foster the development of her two mathematicians and get them engaged in the doing of mathematics.

"Hi girls," she begins. "I was listening in on your conversation and looking at what you have done. I'm so excited about your approach. Could I sit and confer with you on it?"

"Sure!" Both girls are pleased that Eileen is interested in what they have done.

"It looks to me like you started with all these fifteens, 24 of them! But then you did something so nice. You made groups of 60 by putting 4 fifteens together. Was that to make your adding easier?"

"Yep!" both girls nod affirmatively. "And then we did it again here. We made groups of 120," Cassandra continues, pointing proudly to where they have regrouped the 60s into three groups of 120.

"Wow! Was that a clever idea! Smoke is coming out of your heads today!" Eileen exclaims with a grin. She has begun the conferral by ensuring she knows what they have done and then celebrating their approach. Doing so, allows the girls to feel really competent as mathematicians, even brilliant, and they beam ear-to-ear from Eileen's praise. Now she makes her move; she ups the ante and challenges to support further development. "So are you saying that 24x15 = 6x60 = 3x120? These expressions are all equal?"

The girls ponder what Eileen has just said. Their strategy had evolved from just making the addition easier to handle and they had not really thought about it the way Eileen just phrased it. "I guess we are," Scarlett puts forth a response tentatively. Cassandra nods in agreement.

"Wow, because if you are right, this would be an amazing contribution to the community. Your strategy would shorten everyone's work. Instead of writing all the 15s down, we could just write down 6 groups of 60, or 3 groups of 120? Are you sure?" Eileen pushes them to continue considering the equivalence of the expressions. To convince their peers they will need to justify this piece, and the process of justification will also foster their own understanding.

"Yes, it does work!" both girls are now jumping in delight. "See, you just have to put the pieces together like this….just make the groups bigger and then you don't have so many pieces to add up."

Eileen is enjoying their excitement. They own the invention. She has empowered them and gotten them hooked on justifying the regrouping. Maybe she can even get them to consider the associative property. She pushes on, "Let me make sure I understand what you are saying. Wow, this is so exciting. Your strategy is giving me goose bumps! You put 4 of the 15s together in a new group, right? And now you have 6 bigger groups?"

Both girls chorus, "Right!"

"Well let me try writing something to make sure I understand. Is this what you mean?" Eileen writes:

$$24 \times 15 = (6 \times 4) \times 15$$

Then she continues, "Instead of doing 24 groups you thought of the 24 as 6 groups of 4 fifteens? I've put the parentheses around the 6 x 4, just to show that it came from the 24. Mathematicians use parentheses like this to let their audience know which pieces they did first. And then (6 x 4) x 15 became 6 x (4 x 15)? Does this represent what you did?" She writes:

$$(6 \times 4) \times 15 = 6 \times (4 \times 15)$$

She pauses to let the girls think a bit, as she knows they will need time to ponder the representation that she has put forth in the form of an equation. Note also how naturally she has introduced the use of parentheses as she represented their ideas.

The girls ponder the representation for a few minutes, and then slowly Scarlett begins to recognize the connection between the representation and what they did. "It is!" she exclaims with growing delight to Cassandra. "I think the 4 just moved!"

Eileen, now feeling quite pleased, pushes on towards the generalization of the associative property. "This is so interesting! When you turned 6 x 60 into 3 x 120, did you move a number, too?" To support reflection on this question, she writes, (3 x 2) x 60 = 3 x (2 x 60), and then comments, "I have to confer with some other kids now, but I would love you both to talk about this in our congress later. Would you make a poster about it, a poster that would be convincing to the other kids? I'll check back with you later on this, ok? Wow, very exciting."

Characteristics of a Good Conferral

Note the mentoring that has occurred in this rerun of the conferral. Eileen has actually not asked as many open-ended general questions as in the first scenario in Chapter One. And, her questions are more than just "why" questions; they are targeted. She begins by listening carefully and noting what is on their paper. She makes sure she understands what they are doing by asking them if her understanding is correct, and then she celebrates a big idea in their work: groups can be regrouped and the product stays the same. This move builds confidence and fosters the development of a positive growth-mindset.

Next she gets "underneath" their strategy and ups the ante; she raises the bar. She helps illuminate the associative property for consideration by writing a crisp representation of it in equation form, but directly links it to what they did. She does not explain the associative property to them, but leaves them to develop a justification to present to their fellow mathematicians during a subsequent congress.

In the congress, there will be opportunities to discuss the property further and to work towards the generalization of it. For now, the two mathematicians need time to work on justifying it and to think about how they will convince their audience. Then she leaves them to work on more mathematics. Most importantly, note that the children will own the mathematics when they share it in the subsequent congress. It will be *their* story to tell; not hers.

Knowing what to celebrate, what to get under and support, what is worth discussing and what isn't, and when and how to challenge is not a simple matter. This knowledge comes from a deep understanding of the mathematical practices and the development of the mathematics at hand—in this case multiplication. Where does that knowledge come from?

It is tempting to see ourselves as either a literature or math person and to feel that we might never be able to develop the competency of conferring in math well—that maybe we were born without a math gene. But remember the quote of John Green's in the epigraph, "The vast majority of us imagine ourselves as literature people or math people. But the truth is that the massive processor known as the human brain is neither a literature organ, nor a math organ. It is both and more." Research shows that all humans are born with the propensity to learn language and to do mathematics. It is only our past schooling that may have convinced us otherwise.

In the next chapter, we'll examine the development of multiplication together. This was the framework employed in the rerun. Understanding of a developmental trajectory—a landscape of learning—can serve as a powerful lens for analysis of children's work and as a tool to use when conferring. Every topic in mathematics has a landscape associated to it, because all learning, whether writing or mathematics, is about development.

Chapter Three

* * *

Conferring to Support the Development of Multiplication

Mathematics is not a careful march down a well-cleared highway, but a journey.

—W. S. Anglin

The Landscape

Before you start reading this chapter, test yourself. Make a list of strategies you've seen children use for multiplication problems. What might a developmental progression of them look like? Which develops first? Are there any precursors to others? What big ideas and models do you think are important in the development of multiplication? After you have made your list read on and see how you did.

If you want to see a short video of Cathy explaining and building the multiplication landscape, go to http://tiny.cc/NPO2 or scan the QR Scan Code provided here:

The video is provided courtesy of www.NewPerspectivesOnline.net.

When children are first introduced to problems requiring multiplication, they have ways to solve them even if no one has ever shown them how. They model the problem, usually employing manipulatives of some sort, or a drawing, and then to get an answer they use a strategy they already know—counting. They make groups, count the objects in each group, count the number of groups to make sure they have the right quantity, and then to produce the product they start all over again, counting the whole arrangement by ones until they reach a total. Let's call this tedious counting strategy *counting 3 times*.

Precisely because this approach is so tedious, as children construct the idea that each group has the same number of objects they come to realize that counting 3 times is inefficient and unnecessary. They begin to mark the last number in a group as they count, often by saying it louder and pausing, and soon the strategy of *skip counting* evolves. Now, rather than counting every object, they make equal groups first and count using only the multiples. For example, to figure out the cost of a set of six 5-cent stamps, children will say, "5, 10, 15, 20, 25, 30."

Closely related to skip counting is the strategy of *repeated addition* where they write all the fives down and add them up. But, the strategy of repeated addition presents a new dilemma—*how* to add all of the fives up. At first they skip count, but soon reflection on the inefficiency and difficulty of this strategy causes the construction of a new big idea—*groups can be regrouped* to make the addition (or skip counting) easier and the sum will still be the same! This new insight is a major point in development, as its construction now opens the door for several new possibilities.

Some children may put 2 fives together to make a ten and then skip count by tens. Now they have 3 tens and the big idea of equivalence can be examined: $6 \times 5 = 3 \times 10$. For a young third grade mathematician this is a major insight! The six has halved and is now 3, and the five has doubled and is now 10. A new strategy *doubling and halving* emerges, as well as another big idea: *one expression can be exchanged for another because they are equivalent*.

Some children may decide to regroup by putting 3 fives together, and then double the result. Rather than producing 6 x 5 = 3 x 10, they produce 2x15. The six has now been divided by 3 and the 5 has been tripled! The strategy of *thirding and tripling* is under construction, while a new big idea based on the generalization of these strategies begins to appear on the horizon—the *associative property*.

The associative property may at first be out of reach to most. It will take time for children to come to realize that as the groups are being regrouped fewer groups are needed, and the amount in the group is proportionally related. For example, initially the 6 was thought of as 3 groups of two if children paired two fives together. A representation in equation form of this thinking is:

$$(3 \times 2) \times 5 = 3 \times (2 \times 5)$$

Originally the factor of 2 was associated with the 3; later it was associated with the 5. When thirding and tripling results from regrouping the groups, the factor 3 is moving:

$$(2 \times 3) \times 5 = 2 \times (3 \times 5)$$

The idea that you can associate factors as you wish without changing the product is the associative property, and it underlies the strategies of doubling and halving, and tripling and thirding. It is the generalization, and therefore a big idea.

Conferring to Support this Development

Teachers who are knowledgeable of this development are listening intently in a conferral. They are considering what the children are trying to do and celebrating the accomplishments they see. Then they make a move. They up the ante; they challenge. They highlight certain things children may not as of yet noticed, like when Eileen (in the rerun of the conferral in Chapter Two) celebrated the idea that groups can be regrouped, first, and then upped the ante to focus on equivalence:

"It looks to me like you started with all these 15s, 24 of them! But then you did something so nice. You made groups of 60 by putting 4 of them together. Was that to make your adding easier?"

"Yep! And then we did it again here. We made groups of 120." Cassandra points to where they have regrouped the 60s into 3 groups of 120."

"Wow! Was that a clever idea! Smoke is coming out of your heads today!" Eileen exclaims with a grin.

She has begun the conferral by celebrating what they have done. Doing so allows the girls to feel really competent as mathematicians, even brilliant, and they beam ear-to-ear from Eileen's praise. Now she makes her move; she ups the ante. "So are you saying that $24 \times 15 = 6 \times 60 = 3 \times 120$? These expressions are all equal?"

Moves like this are what make conferrals powerful—they make the short moments we have with children matter. The questioning ensures progressive mathematical development. It is targeted to produce reflection on ideas just coming into view on the landscape of development.

Let's return to the example of sets of stamps and examine a conferral by me to see this in action. A Quick Scan Code is provided to access the video.

To access the video go to: http://tiny.cc/NPO3 or just scan the QR code:

The video is provided courtesy of **www.NewPerspectivesOnline.net.**

More video of Cathy conferring as well as a full course on conferring taught by her, for which this book can be a reader, is also available on the website.

More Possibilities

Other children may not group the stamps by pairing, but may use a section they know and then add the rest on. For example, they might know the fact, 5 x 5 = 25, and start there. Now they only have one more 5 to add on. This is also a major insight and it, too, saves a lot of skip counting! Here the strategy of using *partial products* is emerging. This means the conferral needs to be different. The generalization of this strategy is not the associative property; it is the *distributive property*. These children are considering how 6 fives can be replaced with 5 fives plus one more 5. The 6 fives are being distributed over addition:

$$6 \text{ x } 5 = (5 \text{ x } 5) + (1 \text{ x } 5)$$

To up the ante, the conferral might continue with, "What an insight! Are you saying that whenever you multiply it is okay to break the first factor up and do easier pieces of the problem first and then add the products of the pieces up? Does this always work? What if you broke the other factor up? Would that work, too? Have you tried it with some other numbers? Like if you wanted to multiply 12 x 5, could you break the 12 into 10 + 2 and do 10 x 5 and then 2 x 5?" It might also be nice to follow with, "Wow! If you are right, what a contribution to the community this will be! Whenever we have harder problems with bigger numbers we could just break the multiplication up into partial products and add them together? Do you think you could convince the community of this?"

Still other children may not regroup at all; they may model the problem as a rate. At first their representation may be very tedious and directly linked to skip counting. They may write: 1 stamp costs 5 cents; 2 stamps cost 10 cents; 3 stamps cost 15 cents; etc. Even though the strategy is tedious, note the ratio thinking of stamps to cost. Here the conferral should go in a different direction because coming into view is the big idea of *proportional reasoning.*

If we begin the conferral with a celebration over the ratios the students are recording and then get underneath the strategy, we can up the ante with a move that may support *doubling* and later more generalized *scaling.* It is easier at first for learners to mentally regroup groups and double, than to do a more generalized scaling. So, the conferral might start with, "Wow, this is such a great way that you are keeping track of the number of stamps and the cost! I'm wondering if your strategy might even be able to be shortened. If you know that 2 stamps cost 10 cents, could you figure out the cost of 4 stamps without even needing to do 3 stamps? And I bet you could even use your strategy to figure out bigger sets like 8 or 16! Wow, check it out and let me know!" This move is supportive of doubling, the earliest form of scaling.

Later, more generalized scaling could be supported by the questions, "If you know that the cost of 1 stamp is 5 cents, what would 10 stamps cost? If you know the cost of 10, could you use that to figure out the cost of 9, or 5?"

Knowing which Model to Introduce and When

Representation is a critical part of doing mathematics and so, as we confer, it can also be beneficial to introduce models as tools for thinking where appropriate. In the case of emerging proportional reasoning, a t-chart can be useful.

Mentors make suggestions but don't tell their mentees what to do. They leave the decision in the hands of the learner. So one might say, "I don't know if you want to try this, or not. You are the mathematicians, so it is your choice, but there is a model that adult mathematicians use sometimes when they are doing a strategy like yours. It is called a t-chart, or a ratio table. They put their data on it so they don't have to write all of the words down. It helps them to examine the data for patterns." Then you might draw a t-chart like this:

Stamps	Cost
1	5 cents
2	10 cents
4	

On the other hand, if learners are not using ratio thinking it may be a better move to suggest that an array or a number line might be a useful tool. Both of these models are powerful representational tools for supporting children to move from using repeated addition, to using doubling and halving or partial products (see Figures 3.1 and 3.2).

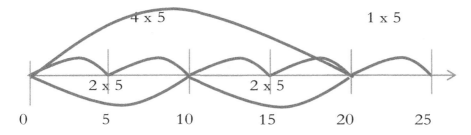

Figure 3.1
Using Partial Products: 5 x 5 = (4 x 5) + (1 x 5)

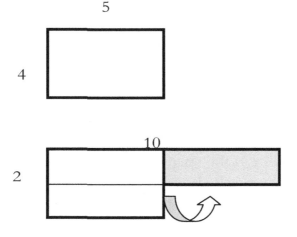

Figure 3.2
Doubling and Halving: 4 x 5 = 2 x 10

The array is particularly helpful as a tool to examine the commutative property (see Figure 3.3).

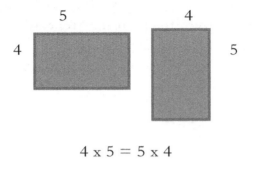

$$4 \times 5 = 5 \times 4$$

Figure 3.3
An Example of the Commutative Property on the Array

Summing Up

The introduction of possible representational tools for thinking in a conferral at just the right moment, yet offering choice to keep the young mathematicians at the helm, supports mathematical development. Moves like these encourage children to use models as powerful tools for thinking. They also build feelings of confidence and competence, thereby contributing to a positive growth-mindset. They are good examples of "conscious mentoring" of young apprentices, in contrast to simply just "asking questions to facilitate learning."

As Anglin so aptly put it in the epigraph to this chapter, "Mathematics is not a careful march down a well-cleared highway, but a journey." Precisely because learning *is* development, we are building meaning as we engage in the doing of mathematics.

In this chapter we examined the development of multiplication and saw how knowledge of a developmental trajectory can be a helpful lens as we mentor young mathematicians at work. Every topic in mathematics has a landscape of learning. In the next couple of chapters we'll explore a few more.

Chapter Four

✳ ✳ ✳

Conferring to Support the Development of Early Number Sense and Addition

In most sciences one generation tears down what another has built and what one has established another undoes. In mathematics alone each generation adds a new story to the old structure.

—Hermann Hankel

The Landscape

Make a list to test yourself again before you read on. This time make a list of some big ideas, strategies, and important models for early number sense and addition. Then, as before, see how you did. A description of the development follows and a video clip is also available.

If you want to see a short video of Cathy explaining and building the landscape described here, go to http://tiny.cc/NPO4 or scan the QR code below:

The video is provided courtesy of
www.NewPerspectivesOnline.net

Many researchers (for example see Dehaene, 1997; Carey, 1999) have now accumulated much evidence to support the statement that early number sense is likely innate. As close to birth as we can test, young infants are able to discriminate between 1, 2, and 3 objects and they will even search for missing objects. For instance, if they are shown 3 objects being placed in a box, and then one object is removed without them witnessing the removal and thus they only find 2, they will continue searching for the missing object.

This ability to discriminate between small amounts is called *subitizing*— the sets are perceived as different wholes. Infants are obviously not counting, nor have they developed mathematical language or symbols, but they are able to discriminate small amounts, one from another.

Using this innate knowledge as a foundation, early childhood teachers should build the *5-structure* next. One way to do that is to use a 5-bead rekenrek **(www.Mathrack.com)** and show quick images, for example of 2 and 3, 4 and 1, etc. This supports the development of an understanding of the *cardinality* and *conservation* of 5—if none are added or removed the amount remains the same even when the parts shown are different. Five is the amount of the group, not the name of the last bead. See Figure 4.1.

Figure 4.1
The 5-bead rekenrek showing 2 + 3 = 5

Developing the 5-structure is critical to the development of early number sense and later addition, as 7 can then be seen on the 10-bead rekenrek as 5+2. Similarly, 8 can be seen as 5+3, and 9 can be seen as 5+4. Since the white beads remaining on the right are also few enough to be *subitizable*, the 10-bead rack also provides support to develop the *combinations that make ten*.

Compensation and *equivalence* are two big ideas that underlie the combinations that make ten and they are also supported by the rack: 5+5 can be turned into 6+4, which in turn can be turned into 7+3, by just moving a bead. And, of course, the big idea of *associativity* is related to compensation as it is really an amount that is being moved from one addend and associated with another. We can always associate that amount with either addend, and the sum stays the same: $(5+2) + 3 = 5 + (2+3)$. See Figure 4.2.

Figure 4.2
The 10-bead rekenrek showing 5+2 = 7 and 7+3 = 5+5

Once children are familiar with the rekenrek and show evidence of being able to prioritize the 5 and 10-structures (they no longer count every bead but move the 5 red in one move), you can progress to the use of the 20-bead rack. This rack supports children to make use of two more strategies as they journey towards the development of automaticity of the basic facts. On the rack, *doubles* appear with a 10-structure built in. See Figure 4.3. And once the doubles are familiar, children use them for *near doubles*. For example, 8+7 might be solved as 7+7+1.

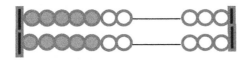

Figure 4.3
The 20-bead rekenrek showing 7+7 = 10+4

A second important addition strategy to develop is the *making of a ten*. This strategy grows out of the use of associativity and compensation. An example is the substituting of 10+6 for the harder problem of 9+7. Children remove one bead from the 7 and associate it instead with the 9.

Thus, the 9 has now been made into a 10, and the 7 has become 6. Both expressions are equal and the result is this equation: $9+7 = 10+6$.

As children move beyond early number sense to the development of strategies for later addition with larger numbers, they employ the use of all of the ideas and strategies they have been developing as they worked earlier to get the basic facts automatic—the stories they told for smaller amounts, become the grist of new stories they can tell about larger amounts. They decompose addends and *take jumps of ten and adjust:*

$$32 + 19 = 32 + 20 - 1$$

or sometimes they decompose and use a piece of it to *get to a landmark number :*

$$32 + 19 = 32 + 8 + 11$$

Both of these strategies make use of the big ideas developed earlier: compensation, associativity, and equivalence.

Sometimes children decompose both addends, *splitting* the numbers apart using expanded notation:

$$32 + 19 = 30 + 2 + 10 + 9$$

Although this strategy is a precursor to the development of place value and eventually the standard carrying algorithm, it produces a lot of partial sums to keep track of and thus is usually not very efficient. When the splitting strategy is first constructed by children it can be celebrated, but children should also be nurtured and supported to develop and make use of the other more easily-used strategies for mental arithmetic, for example the strategies described in the prior paragraph.

Conferring to Support this Development

As we witnessed in the examples of conferrals in the two previous chapters, teachers who are knowledgeable of development begin a conferral by listening intently for the related landscape. The conversation is usually structured into three parts: 1) consider what the children are trying to do and make sure you understand it; 2) celebrate the accomplishments you see; and then, 3) up the ante—challenge with something for them to work further on.

Let's enter a first grade class during math workshop and study some conferrals in action. See if you can find the three sections. The first conferral is available here. Use the Quick Scan Code to see a conferral of the author with two first graders, as they work on investigations from the CFLM unit *The Double-Decker Bus.*

*To see a video of Cathy conferring with two first graders go to **http://tiny.cc/NPO5** , or scan the QR code provided here:*

*The video is provided courtesy of **www.NewPerspectivesOnline.net.***

More video of Cathy conferring as well as a full course on conferring, for which this book can be a reader, is also available on that website.

Let's also examine another example. Debbie Katzburg, a teacher in Southern California, is conferring with two of her young mathematicians, Ricardo and Juan, as they work on an investigation from the CFLM unit *Farms and Fences*. Ricardo and Juan have built a fence with 16 purple and 16 white Cuisenaire Rods. The purple rods are each 4 cm. long, and the white rods are each 1 cm. long. The boys are trying to determine the overall length of their fence.

Debbie: I've been listening and watching as you worked. May I sit and confer with you a bit? I noticed you are working on the eggplant farmer's fence. He used 16 purple sections and 16 white sections, didn't he. And I see that you have placed these all in a nice line and you are keeping track in your math journals on an open number line to show how far you are, just like we did in the minilesson. Wow. That is so terrific. What a great idea to record like that so you can keep track of how far you are. *(They have placed all the purple ones in a line, followed by the white ones).* So you are working on the purple first and I see that on your number line you have written 4, then 8, then 12, and it is getting hard, isn't it? I agree! Counting by fours *is* hard! I wonder if the eggplant farmer actually put all the purples together or if a different design might have made it easier to keep track?

Ricardo: Hey, maybe we could do purple, white, purple, white…. And if we keep going like that it would be a pattern. That would be a pretty fancy fence.

Juan: Yeah. That's nice!

Debbie: OK, that is pretty, but is it easier to add it up?

Ricardo: Four and a white makes five, then 4 more is…… 9, then 1 is 10….. let's mark this down on the line so we don't forget, Juan.

(Debbie lets the pair get that down on the line and then she challenges.)

Debbie: So let me see if I know what you have done so far. You said 4 and 1 was 5? Is the next purple and white also 5?

Ricardo: *(pondering for a minute)* Yes. 5 + 5 is 10. That's what we got.

Juan: Hey, this is going to be a good design. So purple, white, purple white....that's another 10, so now we are up to 20. We can keep going by tens! That's easy!

Debbie: Wow! That is a cool strategy! You are making your fence into fives and tens....that is a lot easier than adding on fours, isn't it? But, is it ok to do that? If we move numbers around when we add to make the work easier, do we still get the same answer?

Juan: I think so...

Debbie: Why don't you and Ricardo work on this a bit? See if you are right, and if you are, think about how you can convince the other kids.

Reflection and Analysis

Note how both Debbie and I first make sure that we understand what the students are doing. We need to do that first to know what to celebrate and how to challenge. In the conferral on the Vimeo clip, my goal became to support the development of compensation, associativity, and equivalence as the boys worked to find efficient ways to make equivalent arrangements using the top and the bottom of a double-decker bus.

Debbie is working on the same big ideas in the context of building fences. The boys have drawn a line to represent the fence and are marking the fence sections on it. The representation is similar to an open number line and the boys are using it as a tool to help them keep track. Debbie celebrates their use of this model, but continues examining their addition strategy to make sure she understands *how* they are using the model.

Their addition strategy is very cumbersome and difficult for them. They are adding all the fours first, trying to skip count. Children will often do this when they have a lot of addends; they proceed in a linear fashion moving left to right adding on each time and don't think to recombine the numbers (associativity) to make use of friendlier expressions. As Debbie proceeds with the conferral she works to support the development of associativity, by specifically focusing on the use of the 5- and 10-structures as landmarks.

Knowledge of the landscape affects every move that we make. Our questions are consciously targeted to promote development, yet we try never to make the children feel that we have a strategy we want them to use. We want the children to *own* the invention; *they* are doing the math. Ownership of the strategies, the big ideas, and the ways of modeling problems must remain with the mathematicians during a conferral. Ownership is critical in building self-confidence and a positive growth mind-set. Ultimately it is ownership of the mathematics that will promote and result in solving problems with tenacity and confidence. We are mentoring, working *with* these young students as *they* do mathematics. The mood and tenor are collaborative—it is a conversation that flows back and forth.

Debbie gets underneath Juan and Ricardo's strategy and uses the context of colored fence sections to support a resequencing of the addends. This move engenders a focus on associativity and promotes the use of the strategy: getting to a landmark number. It does not feel like Debbie has an answer she wants the boys to get, or that she is testing them or probing with a barrage of "why" questions. In fact, had they started with a different strategy, Debbie's questions would have been different. Note how my conferral is similar.

Taxonomies that characterize types of questions, like Bloom's (1971) or Gagne's (1965), are not helpful when questioning and conferring, as they are not about mentoring within a specific discipline; they are about classifications of types of general questions. Categories of question types and lists of general questions to use are not specific enough to support progressive mathematical development. Let's keep this in mind and examine one more conferral on addition, this time in a second grade classroom.

More Possibilities

Aisha Smith, a second grade teacher in New York, is in the midst of the CFLM unit *The T-shirt Factory*. She notes as she moves around the room that two students, Yolanda and Paul, have used expanded notation, splitting each addend up as they work to calculate the total number of size-small t-shirts stored in their warehouse inventory. To find the total of 38+43+19 they have written on their paper:

$$30 + 8 + 40 + 3 + 10 + 9$$

Using arrows to show their steps, they work first with the 30+40, and then add on 10 more. Next, they work with the remaining units, adding 8+3 to get 11, and then adding on 9 more. Lastly, they combine the two partial sums, 80+20, resulting in a final, correct answer of 100. They have used a *splitting* strategy; they have decomposed the numbers using expanded notation and made several partial sums, working first with the tens, then the units. Aisha sits to confer.

Aisha: Wow. This looks so interesting! May I sit and confer with you? (*Both children respond affirmatively with smiles and Aisha pulls over a chair and sits down.*) So what I think is so nice is that you have broken each of the numbers up and then recombined them! You also showed on your paper where the parts came from. 38 *is* 30 + 8, and that is so terrific that you know that! The 3 *is* 3 bundles of ten t-shirts and you knew that was 30. Next I think you then added all of your parts up doing the biggest amounts (the bundles) first, and then the loose ones. Is that right? Do I understand what you did?

Yolanda: (*Grinning broadly and showing pleasure that her teacher understands their thinking*) Yes, that's what we did. It made it easier for us.

Aisha: That's terrific, because mathematicians do like to find easier ways. Don't they? They think it is a very pretty solution when they make a problem simpler! You are doing some lovely mathematics here! (*Both children are smiling broadly under her praise, and now Aisha ups the ante.*) I'm even wondering if there is a way to do it in fewer steps, but I don't know. Let me know what you think about this. May I draw something on your paper first, to help me keep track of all of your steps? You have a lot of steps and I want to make sure I understand them all and don't forget any! (*Aisha draws an open number line showing all the jumps: 30 + 40 + 10 + 8 + 3 + 9 as shown in Figure 4.4.*) Did I get them all? Wow! You worked hard. That was a lot of steps to remember!

Paul: It was for us, too! That's why we wrote down everything, to help us keep track!

Aisha: (*Smiling and acknowledging their hard work*). It seems in your strategy that you like using landmark numbers, like 30, 40, and 10. That's a really smart choice. I do, too! It makes it easier to use friendly numbers like those, when you have a lot of pieces, doesn't it. You said 38 could be thought of as 30 + 8, but it is also near to 40, too. I'm wondering if that could be helpful. How many are we missing to get to 40?

Paul: Yeah! That's a good idea. We just need 2 more and we could take them from the 43. And then, 40 + 41, I already know, because I know a double, 40 + 40 = 80, so just one more. That makes 81. Wow. That's easy.

Yolanda: And now we could use the 9 from the 19 to get to 90, and 10 more gets us to the same answer, 100.

Aisha: Oh my, gosh! Wow! I think this way even has fewer steps than what you did before. And, did you just do that in your heads? Yikes! That is amazing. Do you think you could make a poster about this for our math congress later, and convince the rest of the kids? Maybe you could draw a number line for this strategy, too, and count the steps like we did before with your first strategy. I need to go confer with some other kids right now, but let me know what you come up with, ok? This is so exciting!

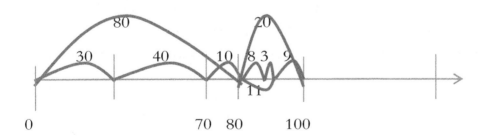

Figure 4.4
A Representation of Splitting on the Open Number Line

Reflection and Analysis

Different Places, Different Moves

Aisha asks different questions than Debbie (and I), because the math at hand and under construction is different—her learners are at different places on the landscape. Yolanda and Paul started by using a splitting strategy. Although a precursor to an understanding of place value, the strategy demands that they keep track of a lot of pieces and for this pair that made paper and pencil required tools.

Associativity, compensation, and equivalence are again being reused by this pair, too, as these big ideas underlie all additive decomposition and recombining. But conversing on these ideas will not be helpful in fostering further development, as the children have already developed a firm understanding of them. Higher on the landscape is the strategy of keeping one addend whole and efficiently using pieces to move to a landmark. This strategy allows them almost to do all of the adding mentally.

It was knowledge of the landscape that helped Aisha know where to go with her questioning. And when examining the steps on an open number line model one can see how the memory load is much less. See Figure 4.5.

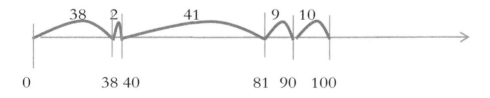

Figure 4.5
A Representation of Keeping one Addend Whole and Moving to a Landmark

45

Knowing Which Model to Introduce and When

Aisha introduced the open number line model as a tool for thinking. This was a decision based on an understanding of development, as well. The rekenrek was discussed earlier in this chapter as a helpful model to use to develop the 5 and 10 structures and that is the model I was using in the first conferral on early number sense. The numbers were under 20, and the rack was an appropriate model to use to explore compensation and equivalence.

As Debbie worked with accumulated distances of fence sections, the Cuisenaire Rods were used to help emerge the open number line model, and it is the open number line that Aisha uses also. The choice of model when introducing one in a conferral is critical. Some models are only helpful in producing correct answers. Children can manipulate cubes and base ten blocks, or move on a hundreds chart, and then read the answer off of the model. They count, manipulate rods, or move across rows or down columns and read the answer off the result of their actions on the model. This "reading-off" behavior is not conducive to development, only to getting a correct answer (Beishuizen, 1993; Klein, Beishuizen, and Treffers, 2002).

In contrast, when using the open number line, children cannot read the answer off of the model; they have to think. "If I am at 38, what multiple of 10 am I near; and, how far from it am I?" are the types of questions children must ask themselves. The model is then used to record their thinking as they work—it is used as a tool for thinking (Gravemeijer, 1991, 1999).

Research on the open number line shows that the further children can go out on a number line keeping the numbers proportionally related (in other words having a sense of magnitude and neighboring landmark numbers), the higher their math achievement (Ramani & Siegler, 2008; Booth & Siegler, 2006; Siegler & Booth, 2004). The ability to use it as a tool for thinking is also positively correlated with attempting and solving non-routine problems (Booth, 2005). Even the playing of board games with tracks has been shown to raise achievement, as the track is similar to the number line model (Ramani & Siegler, 2008).

Summing Up

In the quote in the epigraph to this chapter, Hermann Hankel points out so eloquently how the nature of mathematics requires a building of ideas onto previously developed ones. In his words, "In most sciences one generation tears down what another has built and what one has established another undoes. In mathematics alone each generation adds a new story to the old structure."

In this chapter we witnessed how even very young mathematicians are competently building mathematical structures, and as they go through the years they use the big ideas, strategies, and models they have constructed previously, over and over again.

As we continue into the next chapter and explore the development of subtraction, we will see that the structures children have constructed about number early on will continue to be enriched and the open number line will become a good choice for representing subtraction as well.

Chapter Five

✳ ✳ ✳

Expanding the Structure to Include Subtraction

In most sciences one generation tears down what another has built and what one has established another undoes. In mathematics alone each generation adds a new story to the old structure.

—Hermann Hankel

The Landscape

It is purposeful that the epigraph from Chapter Four has been used again. Without subtraction the story of addition would be incomplete. Test yourself again by making a list. What does the development of subtraction entail?

Subtraction is the inverse of addition and to really understand number as a quantity made up of parts, the relationships of the parts to the whole—the structure—must be constructed. If two parts make up a whole and one is removed, the other remains.

To see a video of Cathy describing and building the landscape for subtraction, go to http://tiny.cc/NPO6 or use the QR code provided here:

The video is provided courtesy of
www.NewPerspectivesOnline.net.

Early in development, however, children have not yet developed this understanding. The context of the problem has a powerful effect on the strategy used when they are first introduced to problems that require subtraction (Carpenter et. al, 1999). With removal type problems (I had $42 and I spent $14; how much do I have left?) children usually *count backwards*. In contrast, if asked to solve a difference or missing addend type problem (Susie has $14 and Joey has $42; how much more does Susie need so they both have the same amount?), they usually *count on*.

Precisely because these counting strategies are so tedious, as children construct the big idea that *subtraction and addition are related* they begin to *look to the numbers first* and count back when the subtrahend is small even though the context may be suggestive of counting on (see the prior example about Susie and Joey), and they will count on when the subtrahend is close to the minuend even when the problem is suggestive of removal. For example, if the numbers are changed in the first problem (I had $42 and I spent $36; how much do I have left?), although the context earlier would have generated a counting backwards strategy, children will now count on from the 36 as this is more efficient—it requires less counting.

It is a deep understanding of the *part/whole relations* involved that fosters the development of the relationship of subtraction to addition, and this structuring of number relations by children is a major landmark in their development. Without the construction of this big idea, context will continue to affect the strategies children use and their strategies will often be inefficient.

When children are removing amounts, one of the ways they make their work more efficient is to *take jumps of tens backwards and adjust*. For example, with the problem 32-19 = ? they might take 20 away and then adjust by adding 1 back in at the end. Or, they may *move to a landmark first* by taking 2 away first to get to 30, take 10 away from the 30, and then remove the remaining 7. With missing addend or difference problems they may use the related addition strategies as they develop them, to replace the counting on. For example they might start at 19, take a jump of 10 first and then add 3, or add 1 first to get to 20, and then add 12, each of these strategies resulting in a total difference of 13.

These are all wonderful mental math strategies, in time developing the ability for many calculations to be done without paper and pencil—an important skill in the era of calculators where we need to be able to look at the answer and know if it is reasonable or not.

Children also attempt *splitting* strategies for subtraction, just as they did with addition. They use expanded notation and calculate partial differences. And once again, although it is a precursor to the standard regrouping algorithm and can be celebrated as employing the use of place value, because there are so many pieces to keep track of, children can become confused over whether to subtract or add pieces. For this reason, splitting is not a particularly helpful strategy most of the time for mental arithmetic.

Probably the most efficient strategy for mental arithmetic when subtracting (but of course it depends on the numbers) is the use of *constant difference*. Adding (or subtracting) the same number to both the minuend and the subtrahend keeps the difference between the two numbers the same, for example, 32-19 = 33-20. The expression on the right is equivalent to the one on the left and thus it can be exchanged for the 32-19, and the use of it makes the problem much easier to calculate.

Conferring to Support this Development

Michael Galland, a third grade teacher from New York, is exploring age differences with his students as they work with the CFLM unit *Ages and Timelines*. Michael has shared data to the class on the ages of the members of his family. He is 31 and his mom is 55. He wonders how old his mom was when he was born and also, now that he is 31, how many years it will be until he reaches the age of 55. The children investigate these two questions as well as several others. A video clip of Michael's conferral with two of his students, Brianda and Domenica, is provided.

As you view the clip, note the moves Michael makes to support the development of constant difference. Note also how he ensures in the beginning that both children are engaged and how he uses the context to help them make sense of the relations they notice. At the end of the conferral he invites them to build an argument to convince the other children in the community. When he leaves them to confer with others, they are engaged: they own the strategy and now it is up to them to convince others of their discovery. And, as young mathematicians at work, they are driven to do so.

To see Michael's conferral, go to *http://tiny.cc/NPO7*, or use the QR scan code provided here:

The video is provided courtesy of
www.NewPerspectivesOnline.net

Summing Up

In this chapter we've examined how the development of the content drives the questions. "In most sciences," Hankel explains in the epigraph, "one generation tears down what another has built and what one has established another undoes. In mathematics alone each generation adds a new story to the old structure."

As teachers, it is important that we start our conversations with children on the mathematical stories they are trying to develop—on the structures they are trying to build. The stories they tell today will form the structures for the new stories they become able to tell tomorrow. Adding an understanding of the operation of subtraction to their addition stories develops a much richer number structure.

Thus, there are no magic-bullet questions that can be used across conferrals, as powerful conferrals always begin with what the young mathematicians before us are trying to do. And, each mathematics topic that we are required to teach has an associated landscape that describes the development of it. Knowledge of these landscapes and respect for the children with whom we work are characteristics of every powerful conferral, and each should be generative over time of the development of new structures if we make the moments matter. In the next chapter, we'll examine the development of fractions and then study some conferrals in action on this topic.

Chapter Six

* * *

Conferring to Support the Development of Fractions

When things get too complicated, it sometimes makes sense to stop and wonder: Have I asked the right question?

—Enrico Bombieri

The Landscape

Why are fractions so difficult for so many people? Have you ever wondered about that question? Perhaps they are for you, too. If so, have you blamed yourself, thinking the content was just too difficult, and you just weren't as smart as some of your other, seemingly more mathematically-oriented, friends?

To see a video of Cathy describing and building the landscape for fractions, go to http://tiny.cc/NPO8, or scan the QR code provided here.

The video is provided by courtesy of
www.NewPerspectivesOnline.net.

Perhaps it is not that the content is difficult, but that the way you were taught about fractions was not helpful. Fractions can be introduced as part-to-parts relations, as fair sharing division, or as a number on a number line between 0 and 1. Does it matter which model we use first? Is there a developmental progression that might be more conducive to the fostering of an understanding of fractions than another? These are very important questions for us to ask.

Most early childhood programs introduce fractions by using a part-to-parts model. For example, children are often given pattern block activities to do and, as they build shapes with the blocks, teachers label the green triangle as 1/6 of the yellow hexagon (since 6 triangles fit into the whole) and the red trapezoid as ½ (since only two fit into the whole), etc.

Or, teachers might use geometric shapes, such as circles or rectangles, and cut them into equal parts and label them, explaining that 1 part out of 4 parts equals ¼. In later grades, fraction bars are often used to introduce addition and subtraction with the part-to-parts shown on the strips.

Research shows that the model we start our instructional sequences with does make a difference. Starting fraction work with a part-to–parts model creates the misconception that we often see: that 1/8 is larger than 1/7 because 8 is a larger number than 7. Children leap to this erroneous conclusion since there are more parts (8 vs. 7). For a deep understanding of fractions to develop, the big idea that needs to be constructed early on is: *the greater the number of pieces, the smaller the piece.*

A second big idea is also critical—*the whole matters.* For example, ¼ of 2 is a larger piece than ¼ of 1; and, it is possible for ⅕ to be larger than ¼ if the wholes they refer to are different—⅕ of 1 is larger than ¼ of ½. As teachers, we have probably all seen children who, in trying to cut 3 equal pieces out of a rectangle or circle, struggle because thirds are difficult to make equally. As they work, children often cut out an approximation of 3 equal pieces as best they can, and then overlay the pieces and cut slivers off to make them congruent. They throw the scraps away and argue vehemently that they have thirds because they have 3 equal pieces and each piece is one out of the 3 equal pieces. This conclusion fits with their definition of fractions, if they have been introduced to fractions with a part/parts model: 1 out of 3 equal parts *is* ⅓. However, the piece is not ⅓ of the original whole because they have thrown some of it away. The whole matters!

Conferring to Support this Development

A video clip is available here for you to observe Carol Mosesson-Teig conferring with her fifth graders as they work on an investigation about the fair sharing of sub sandwiches. The investigation is from the CFLM unit *Fieldtrips and Fundraisers:* 4 children shared 3 subs; 5 children shared 4 subs; 8 children shared 7 subs; and 5 children shared 3 subs. Within each group the sharing was done fairly. But, was it fair across the groups? Did the children in one group get more of a sandwich to eat than the children in another, assuming the subs are all the same size? If so, which of the four groups got the most?

To see Carol's conferral go to http://tiny.cc/NPO9, or scan the QR code provided here:

The video is provided courtesy of www.NewPerspectivesOnline.net.

As Carol confers, take note of how she facilitates a conversation on the ⅕ of the half. At first the children call the slice ⅕ because the half is cut into five equal slices, but as Carol probes they come to realize that the whole matters: the slice is ⅕ of the half, but it is also 1/10 of the whole.

They also come to realize that ⅘ of a sub is equivalent to ½+ 1/10 +⅕. See Figure 6.1.

Figure 6.1
4 subs shared with 5 children, ⅘ = ½ + 1/10 + ⅕

A variety of learning trajectories exist in the research literature in relation to the development of fractions (for example see: Moss and Case, 1999; Confrey et al., 2009; Streefland, 1991; Fosnot and Dolk, 2002).

Most researchers agree that starting instructional sequences with the development of *fair sharing division,* as Carol is doing, is the best approach. For example, if 4 subs are shared with 4 people (4/4), everyone gets 1, but when 4 subs are shared with only 2 people (4/2) everyone now gets 2 subs each; the denominator halved but the quotient doubled. When 1 sub is shared equally with 2 people everyone gets ½; and when a sub is shared equally with 4 people everyone gets

¼. Three subs shared equally with 4 people results in ¾ of a sub for each, or ¼ of each sub x 3 subs.

Starting instructional sequences with this model supports the development of several big ideas and strategies on the fraction landscape and simultaneously avoids some of the common misconceptions that develop from the initial use of a part-to-parts model.

With a fair sharing model *equipartitioning* is constructed at the outset—*equal parts don't need to be congruent* (they may differ in shape but be equivalent; see Figure 6.2). If fairly shared, the parts are equal with nothing left remaining of the whole, and therefore *the greater the number of people sharing, the smaller the piece* that everyone gets. In fact, in the prior example about the sub sandwiches, *when the divisor doubled, the size of the piece was halved*, and reciprocally *when the divisor halved the amount of the resulting share doubled*.

Eventually, these ideas develop into generalized *scaling*—multiplying or dividing the dividend (the numerator) and the divisor (denominator) by the same factor results in equivalence.

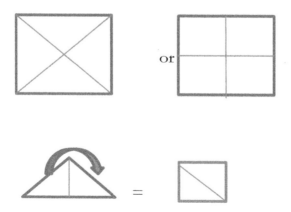

Figure 6.2
Parts Do Not Need to Be Congruent to Be Equal

More Possibilities

All of these big ideas and strategies form a strong foundation for exploring and understanding operations with fractions. I was in a classroom working alongside a 6th grade teacher one day in New York as the children were exploring best buy scenarios from the CFLM unit *Best Buys, Ratios and Rates.* Two girls, Amanda and Clarice, were hard at work trying to figure out which was the better buy: $16 for 20 cans of cat food; or, $8 for 12 cans. I noticed they were discussing two different strategies and trying to decide which approach would be better. Amanda wanted to divide to get the price of one can in each store and Clarice was suggesting that if they used 60 cans as a common whole it would be easier. I sat down to confer.

"I've been listening to your conversation," I began, "And I wanted to sit and confer because I think what you are talking about is *so* interesting! Amanda, you want to compare the price of one can in each store, and Clarice you want to compare the prices for 60 cans. Am I understanding your conversation, correctly?"

I always like beginning a conferral with students in a way that shows I'm genuinely interested in their ideas and want to have a conversation with them, but I also want to be certain that my understanding of their ideas is correct. Using cycles of celebrating and clarifying implicitly tells the girls I'm genuinely intrigued with their thinking—that I'm listening intently, but it also helps me get clarification and determine what to do next. I don't want my conferral to be about just getting them to an answer. I want to support their development as mathematicians, so I'm also asking myself, "What would be helpful to support here? What strategies should I get under and attempt to lift, and what big ideas might I be able to help them construct and generalize?" The landscape is my guide.

"So it seems you are both saying that to compare you need to use a number of cans in common—the same number in each store—and one, or sixty, would work?" I ask. Needing a common whole to compare fractions is a big idea on the landscape and I may be able to use their understanding of it to support them to explore a variety of numbers that might work. They agreed that a common number was important, so I decided to continue getting further clarification, "How would you do the 60 cans Clarice?" I queried.

"Well, I know 3 x 20 is 60, so the price must be 3 x $16. So... $48 for 60 cans. I picked 60 because it was an easy number for me."

"Amanda, what do you think about Clarice's idea," I asked. I wanted to make sure that Amanda was involved, too, and was following the conversation.

"It works but getting 12 to 60 is harder," Amanda offered. "But maybe...." She paused, and then offered, "5 times would work. 5 x 12 is 60, so it's $40 for 60 cans in the other store. It works and that's the best buy."

Noting that the girls seem to have a well-developed sense of scaling to produce equivalent expressions, I decided it was time to up the ante—to challenge them to consider some other possible common wholes. But, first I celebrated what they had done, "Wow, 60 did work! And so nicely! What a great strategy you girls have for comparing!" Then I challenged, "Are there other numbers, too, that might work nicely?"

At first Clarice was quiet, but then with excitement she burst out, "I have a great idea! Instead of making the number of cans the same and comparing the prices, we could make the prices the same and see how many cans we get for that price! If we just double the $8 to $16, we can compare: 12 cans doubled makes 24 cans. So for $16, it is 24 cans compared to 20 cans. That's a fast way!" She exclaimed, beaming, proud of her solution.

"Wow! I knew when I sat down that this was going to be a great conversation! This is amazing what you two are talking about. Are you saying you can scale up, anyway you want, as long as you find a common place to stop? And, the common place can be the number of cans, *or* the money...either way you can compare?" Both girls nodded affirmatively with enthusiasm, quite pleased with what they have come up with. So, I pushed further. "What if we scaled down? Would that work, too?"

"What do you mean?" Amanda looked at me, obviously puzzled.

"Well, I don't know if this will work, but you said we just need a common place to compare. So, in thinking about what you said, I am wondering if the $16 for 20 cans can be scaled to $8 for 10 cans and if we can now compare that to $8 for 12 cans?"

"Yes!" both girls exclaim in unison, grinning broadly.

"Clarice, earlier you had suggested comparing the cost of one can. How were you going to do that? Were you just going to do long division for each?" I decided to query her about this for clarification, because I thought I might be able to support her to consider some other strategies based on proportional reasoning to get to the price of one can, besides using the tedious form of long division.

"Yes," she affirmed my suspicion, so I decided to press on. The tricky thing though would be to support her in a way that encouraged her to change her strategy. And, I needed to leave the ownership of the change with her—to make her feel that it was her insight, not mine.

"I thought so, …and initially I would have done the same thing. But this new approach of yours that you are talking about now has made me wonder if there is a way to use it to get to the price of one can without having to do long division. I've been wondering,… if we had $8 for 10 cans, could we use your strategy of scaling and go from there to 1 can without needing to do long division?"

Now the girls were intrigued and they began working furiously to generate some possibilities. I just listened as they talked. "That would be $4 for 5 cans," Amanda offered.

"And that would be $4 for 6 cans in the other store," Clarice added. "We could even compare there!"

But now Amanda was lost in thought and obviously puzzled. "I want to divide by 5 to get to 1 can, but how do I get the money divided by 5, without doing long division?" she asked me imploringly.

"I don't know if this will help us," I offered an idea, tentatively; wanting to support but at the same time trying to keep her at the helm so she would own the solution, not me. "Sometimes when mathematicians feel stuck, they decide to keep it simple and leave it. They just write down what they know and go on, and sometimes, surprisingly, it helps them later. We might try for now just writing $4/5, over 1. Let's also write down everything else we know so far. That might help us, too. I'll write, but you help me." I wrote down the following: $16/20 = 48/60 = 8/10 = 4/5 = ⅘/1$. "So this is what we know so far. Can we add to our list, I wonder."

"I know $4/5 = .8$. Does that help?" Clarice offered a decimal equivalent, which she knew, but wasn't sure what to do with it.

"So let's add it to our list for now and see," I suggested, and added $.8/1$ to our list of equivalent expressions.

"I just noticed something," Amanda offered with growing excitement. "I think we could have gone from $8/10$ to $.8$, too."

"Let's write it, then." I wrote, $16/20 = 8/10 = .8$. "So what does this $.8$ mean? Is it the price of one can, or what?" Both girls were now thinking hard. Bringing them back to the context had been an important move.

"I think it is," Clarice began. "Because before we had ⅘/1 and the $.8$ equals the $4/5$, so we also could have written down $.8/1$. But, I want to divide to be sure." On her paper she wrote $4 divided by 5 and used the long division algorithm to get a quotient of $.80. "Oh, wow....this makes sense!" she exclaimed. "Look, Amanda. It works! 8 tenths is 80 cents!"

Amanda was excited by their discovery, too, and she was now busy writing. "I'm writing what we know about the other store," she explained. On the paper she had written: $8/12 = 40/60 = 4/6 = 2/3 = ⅔/1$. "I know $2/3$ of a dollar is between 66 and 67 cents because the 6 keeps repeating when you divide. So at the first store one can costs $.80 and at the other store one can costs $.67. Wow, Clarice, we are good! We can use our strategy to divide!" Both girls were now beaming with pride.

And, I was too. I was so proud of them, but I also felt good about my conferral with them. As a result of it their understanding of fractions as division, and their use of scaling as a strategy, had been deepened. This accomplishment needed to be celebrated, and then there was one more challenging question to ask, so I offered: "This is so exciting. This certainly *is* a terrific strategy you have come up with! Will you make a poster about it for the congress? Wow! What a contribution to the community. I can't wait to see how you will convince everyone. How *will* you convince them?" I left them with a smile, to ponder that last question.

Several weeks later I was in their classroom again as their teacher began work on division of fractions. The strong foundation of equivalence and proportional reasoning that they had built earlier was now being generalized to include the operation of division with fractions. They pulled me over and asked if they could explain what they were doing.

Clarice started, "We are using the strategy we used when you were here before. It is so cool. 4/5 divided by 2/3 is equal to 2/5 divided by 1/3. We just halved each fraction so these are still equal."

Amanda explained the next step. Next, we just scaled up by 3, so that gets us to 6/5 divided by 1, and that's the answer!"

I hugged them both with excitement. "Wow, that strategy is a powerful one! I hope it is up on your strategy wall with your names on it!" And sure enough it was. They proudly pointed it out to me, declaring, "And everyone is using it! We convinced everyone!"

Summing Up

Enrico Bombieri offers such a nice quote in the epigraph for us to ponder as we think about conferring, particularly as we move into the middle school and the content becomes more difficult. "When things get too complicated," he says, "it sometimes makes sense to stop and wonder: Have I asked the right question?" He is of course talking about his process of doing mathematics, but the statement as implications for us as teachers, too.

If learners were supported to think problems out in their own ways, imagine how simple the topics we once thought difficult to teach might become. Aligning instructional sequences with the research on the development of the topic, and then conferring in ways that support further development by building on learners' ideas, may be instrumental in producing powerful insights—insights that will inform and transcend beyond the topic at hand to new horizons. When it seems the math is getting more complicated and our learners appear to be struggling with it, it might be best to step back for a moment and ask ourselves, "Have I asked the right question?"

Chapter Seven

* * *

What to Do When Children Get Stuck

Even the greatest mathematicians, the ones that we would put into our mythology of great mathematicians, had to do a great deal of leg work in order to get to the solution in the end.

—Daniel Tammet

Helping Children Get Started

So many people (both adults and children) think that mathematicians are just smart people who know exactly what to do when they start a problem. But the case is just the opposite. In fact, if they do know what to do to get the answer, they say that the problem is trivial and not worth doing at all! It is the challenge of a problem that grips them and they do a great deal of "leg work" before they arrive at a solution. It is tenacity and a positive growth-mindset (Dweck, 2007) that are conducive to eventual success.

Yet, many of the children we work with give up before they start. They seem hooked and even intrigued as we develop contexts to promote inquiry, but when they go off to start working they sit there helpless, saying they don't know what to do. They seek external direction to get started and subsequent approval. How do we help them get started, but perhaps more importantly, how do we change their mindset?

One of the things I have found helpful as I sit to confer with children like these, is to immediately work to dispel the myths they probably have about what it means to do mathematics. I usually start with a comment such as, "I can see you think this problem is a hard one. I agree with you and that is exactly why I thought it would be fun for us all to work on it together! Do you know what mathematicians say when they know what to do to solve the problem right at the start? They say it is a boring problem and not worth doing. To them it's the hard problems that are the interesting ones. I call them the 'juicy ones.' Doing mathematics is like cracking a mystery, being a detective. It's not any fun if you already know a solution. So I guess we have a really juicy, interesting one here, if you are saying you don't even know how to start!"

First I want to acknowledge that the problem is challenging; that I find it so, as well. This changes the power hierarchy from the "all-knowing teacher" and "students who need to figure out what solution the teacher knows and wants" to a community of learners working together to generate interesting insights about the problem at hand. I try to turn their idea of a "math problem" into a "math investigation." This way emphasis is placed on inquiry versus what to do to get an answer.

Secondly, to help learners come to appreciate what it feels like to do mathematics, and to understand and appreciate the process, I use quotes from famous mathematicians about how they feel when doing mathematics. For example I love using this quote from Andrew Wiles, the medal-winning mathematician who cracked Fermat's Last Theorem,

> "Perhaps I can best describe my experience of doing mathematics in terms of a journey through a dark unexplored mansion. You enter the first room of the mansion and it's completely dark. You stumble around bumping into the furniture, but gradually you learn where each piece of furniture is. Finally, after six months or so, you find the light switch, you turn it on, and suddenly it's all illuminated. You can see exactly where you were. Then you move into the next room and spend another six months in the dark. So each of these breakthroughs, while sometimes they're momentary, sometimes over a period of a day or two, they are the culmination of—and couldn't exist without—the many months of stumbling around in the dark that proceed them… However impenetrable it seems, if you don't try it, then you can never do it (2000)."

Another quote I particularly love and frequently use is one by Keith Devlin. He said,

> "When I'm working on a problem it's like climbing a mountain. Sometimes I can't

even see where I'm going. It's just one foot in front of another. And then I reach a point where all of a sudden the vistas open up and I can go down easily for a while, only to eventually reach another climb…."

There are many websites full of quotes by mathematicians. Just google "quotes by mathematicians" and see all the sites that come up. Using quotes like these is a good way to initiate children into the wider community of mathematicians, to really help them feel what the process of doing mathematics is like. Long term I want them to come to appreciate and value the struggle and to develop the tenacity to stick with a problem—to be willing to do the leg work and most importantly to learn to enjoy the process.

I also model what mathematicians do to help get started. I ask children if the problem reminds them of any other problems that seem similar. I ask this frequently because I am trying to encourage children to internalize the question, so that they always begin by reflecting on it. Asking themselves this question every time they start a new problem helps them consider the relationship between problems. Internalizing this question and reflecting on it pushes children to examine the structure of problems so that over time they develop a sense of exemplar problems that can be useful. This helps develop their mathematical intuition.

Many years ago I would begin my summer institutes with the now well-known handshake problem: if everyone at a table introduces themselves and shakes hands with each person at their table, once and only once, how many handshakes would there be, for example if 3 people sat at a table, or 4, or 5, or n? As time went on I found that the problem was being used frequently by many workshop leaders and my students began to tell me that they knew a solution already because they had been in a workshop at their school and their coach had used the same problem. So, I began changing the problem and found to my surprise that even just a slight change in context would disguise the same problem. For example, if I said, "Let's start by introducing ourselves to each other. Find a connection, a unique one (and only one) for each person at your table. For example, with one person you might be from the same town, with another be the same age, and with a third have the same number of children. Find unique connections, one for each person, and have everyone in the group do it with each person. Then think about how many connections there might be for the group if there are 5 people at your table, or 6, or 7, or if you were getting on a plane tomorrow and thought about this same question. Ahead of time you wouldn't know how many people would be on your flight, and of course we all might be getting on planes with differing numbers of people….so let's call the number of people on the plane *n*. How many connections would there be for a group of *n* people?

Another time, I was co-teaching a workshop with my colleague, Bob Washburn, a mathematician at Southern CT State University, and he suggested that we try the problem using the context of points in space: how many line segments would be needed to connect *n* points in space? Even though the group of teachers had just done the handshake problem that morning, and participants had had an extensive congress on a variety of strategies and expressions that they had discovered, few saw a connection at the start and began as if the "points in space problem" were a totally new problem. At this moment, it hit home what Keith Devlin meant when he said, "Many people think mathematicians are smarter than most because when they hit a math problem they often have an intuition of how to start. We aren't smarter, it's just that we have covered more of the terrain and over time we have developed a better sense of the types of problems we might encounter along the journey." Both teachers and the young, developing mathematicians in their classes need many opportunities to explore the terrain and become familiar with it. Encouraging them to explore how problems are related helps develop a sense of the familiar landmarks.

Another thing mathematicians often do is ask themselves if there is a model they think might be useful. Again, because I like encouraging children to do what mathematicians do, I might say, "Sometimes when mathematicians feel really stuck and they don't know how to start, they ask themselves if there is a model that might be a helpful tool. Does any model pop into your mind that you think you could use as tool, maybe one you have used before for problems like this and you found it helpful?"

Very young children might suggest a rekenrek, or for larger numbers an open number line. Ratio tables, graphs, arrays, double number lines can also be helpful tools for multiplication, fractions, and algebra. Even just drawing a picture of the situation is sometimes a way to get unstuck. Helping children to have a first step is important so that they don't give up—they at least have a way to start.

Helping Children Move Past the Hard Places

Getting started does not preclude roadblocks along the way. We need to help children develop tools for those moments as well—things they can try instead of giving up when they hit the hard places. No matter the subject matter, the process of thinking hard about challenging problems will always have its ups and downs. It is learning to respect the process—the creative struggle—that keeps one able to do the necessary leg work to work through the hard places.

I have always loved math, but I also love writing. Several years ago I also took up painting and was surprised to find that the processes I had learned through doing math and writing were similar to what I was now experiencing during the painting process. Some days I could slosh paint onto the canvas so easily and it just felt so right—just what I hoped for happened. Other days I would hit hard places: brush strokes didn't look right; the composition was off; or, the color was just not the right shade. I would work and work and couldn't seem to accomplish anything.

Some days writing flows. It feels easy. Other days getting even a page completed is tortuous. I rewrite the section over and over, trying to find different examples, different words, the right angle to the piece, a better lead. And of course working on a math problem is also no different. Just look at the quotes of Wiles and Devlin at the beginning of this chapter.

I have also learned over time that these hard places are not always bad. They often in fact are places where turning points or eventual breakthroughs will happen and thus punching through them is really important. I've come to understand the process of making meaning, no matter the medium, and I have come to appreciate the struggle.

Runners will describe the same process as well. They get to a place where it feels hard, almost impossible to go one step farther and they have to push and push, and then there is the breakthrough: the adrenaline kicks in and it feels easier for a while, only to eventually hit another climb.

Experiencing the process many times, as well as the exhilaration when you hit the finish line, put the last word to paper, or see the final piece of the solution coming into view, is what enables one to keep going through the hard places. So the question looms: How do we support our developing mathematicians to appreciate the struggle and develop the tenacity to work through the hard places without giving up?

Andrew Wiles said, "When I got stuck and I didn't know what to do next, I would go out for a walk. I'd often walk down by the lake. Walking has a very good effect in that you're in this state of relaxation, but at the same time you're allowing the sub-conscious to work on you. And often if you have one particular thing buzzing in your mind then you don't need anything to write with or any desk. I'd always have a pencil and paper ready and, if I really had an idea, I'd sit down at a bench and I'd start scribbling away."

Sometimes a stretch is helpful—we all need breaks at some point, but teaching children how to allow the subconscious to work during a break is important. Providing kids with a math journal to write down what they have done thus far, suggesting they take a quick stretch but think as they are doing so, advising that they go off for a few minutes alone and write down what they know about the problem thus far and then come back and share with their partner what they wrote, are all helpful suggestions and they communicate what mathematicians do when they get stuck.

When I'm writing I sometimes find it helpful to return to a previous part of the piece and read it over again with a fresh set of eyes. Recrafting some of the less difficult sections allows me to hit the harder place again with a new set of eyes.

When doing mathematics I engage in the same process. I sometimes retrace my earlier thinking to get more solid on what I do know, and then try to go at it again with a firmer ground underneath me. When conferring with kids, you can model this process by getting them to talk about what they do know and where they got stuck. Look for places where you can help them build on what they do know and suggest they use that as a starting place.

A video clip is available of Gary Shevell, the Assistant Principal of PS 116 in New York City, conferring with two third graders Kamren and Zaheer, as they work on figuring out the cost of a set of 24 five-cent stamps. The boys have previously solved for a smaller set of 12 five-cent stamps using skip counting. Using this skip counting strategy however for 24 x 5 had proved to be difficult for them. Watch Gary engage the boys in making use of what they do know—the partial product of 12x5 = 60. In his conferral he helps them work through the difficult place by using something they do know as a starting place.

Lastly, the more problems that children work on, the more they will come to understand the process of doing mathematics. I did a research study many years ago with Marja van den Heuvel-Panhuizen (2001). We studied third, fourth, and fifth graders across two groups: an experimental group where the teachers were using problems from children's lives, every day, to engage them in generating mathematics, and a control group comprised of students from the same schools but whose teachers were using traditional textbooks. We examined strategies and answers of each group and compared them. The gap between groups widened each year with a highly significant difference between groups appearing by grade 5: children in the experimental group used more alternative strategies and attempted far more problems than the control group.

To see Gary's conferral go to **http://tiny.cc/NPO10**, or use the QR scan code provided here:

The video is provided courtesy of **www.NewPerspectivesOnline.net**

Results also showed that a learned helplessness was developing in the control group. If they didn't know how to start on a problem, they just didn't even attempt it. With the experimental group a growth mindset had developed. They believed they could do the problem (even though they didn't always get it right) and so they started. They seemed to have constructed the idea that, as Wiles said, "However impenetrable it seems, if you don't try it, then you can never do it (2000)." They knew they at least had a way to start, and they began.

Summing Up

As we bring this chapter to a close, let's end with another quote from Wiles, "It is fine to work on any problem, so long as it generates interesting mathematics along the way—even if you don't solve it at the end of the day. The definition of a good mathematical problem is the mathematics it generates rather than the problem itself." And the more problems we get children to work on, the more problems they will be willing to begin.

Chapter Eight

∗ ∗ ∗

Conferring to Support the Development of Proof[1]

Don't just read it; fight it! Ask your own questions, look for your own examples, and discover your own proofs. Is the hypothesis necessary? Is the converse true? What happens in the classical special case? What about the degenerate cases? Where does the proof use the hypothesis?

-----Paul R. Halmos
I Want to be a Mathematician, Washington: MAA Spectrum, 1985.

If we are to take seriously the idea of treating young children as emerging mathematicians, then initiating them into a community of rich mathematical discourse centered on proof and argumentation is critical. In contrast to the trivialized school-type activity where children are told, "use words, pictures, and symbols to show your work," young mathematicians at work engage in writing and revising arguments for publication and then in reading and commenting on one another's arguments.

A traditional classroom culture that views mathematics as just arithmetic skills and procedures to be mastered is antithetical to the goals of teaching and learning proof in the

---

[1] Portions of this chapter were previously published in Fosnot and Jacob (2007). Young Mathematicians at Work: Constructing Algebra. Portsmouth, NH: Heinemann. Published here with permission of the authors.

elementary grades. Children need multiple experiences to re-examine, revise, and simplify their ideas, if they are to build a foundation for understanding a mathematician's view of proof. Teaching practices in which children are encouraged to read and question others' ideas, to understand one's own and others' thinking, to develop conjectures and build arguments for these conjectures, and to write or talk about one's reasoning, are all forms of practice that are foundational for building a habit of mind toward proving (Stylianou, Blanton, and Knuth, 2009). When we provide an audience, a reader, and ask children to write up their "proofs" to convince others, shared principles and rules of deduction do begin to be used in a chain, building on each other (Fosnot and Jacob, 2006), and written arguments can take on an early form of proof.

Towards this aim, once children believe they have reached a solution to the problem at hand, they are invited in math workshop to justify their thinking and make a poster for display. The community then engages in a "gallery walk" to review their peers' arguments and to provide feedback in the form of comments on sticky-notes. Gallery walks provide children with opportunities to have their reasoning read and to get review comments from their peers.

With older middle school students we have even involved them in the production of class-edited chapter books of a variety of solutions for a specific problem. For example, one summer I worked alongside teachers in Washington DC in a *Mathematicians in Residence* summer camp for kids. With some 5th graders we produced an edited chapter book on algorithms for division. Small working groups of 3 to 4 kids each wrote a chapter, justifying why an algorithm worked, and when it might be helpful to use it. Some chose models like arrays or ratio tables to examine a procedure, using a specific case but showing how it was generalizable; others built arguments based on the properties of operations. Because the arguments in each chapter were crafted differently, the book created a nice context to discuss argumentation.

As children engage in determining the focus and crafting of a justification for a piece of mathematics to be displayed on a poster in a gallery walk, teachers confer again. However, now the focus of the conferral shifts: rather than discussing strategies to arrive at a solution to a problem (as we examined in prior chapters), the conferring aims at the development of argumentation.

In prior chapters, we've examined landscapes of learning (developmental trajectories) for various topics: multiplication; early number sense, addition, and subtraction; and fractions.

We witnessed how these are helpful tools when conferring as children work. But, as children begin to work on written arguments, a new landscape of learning is needed as a developmental lens—the landscape of proof. In this chapter, that landscape is presented and we'll study teachers using it as they confer. But first, let's look at a bit of history about the development of proof.

The Development of Proof: an historical look

Questioning, defending, justifying, and proving are all processes characteristic of human activity. Even young children engage naturally in these processes. While there are rules of logic that govern a rigorous notion of mathematical proof, the idea of proof has its genesis in natural human activity, in the need to establish certainty, and to convince others (Stylianou, Blanton, and Knuth, 2009). Professional mathematicians acquire their understanding of what proof is through participation in their community. To them, proof involves rigorous reasoning, without gaps; it is a form of argumentation that establishes the validity of a mathematical statement based on clearly formulated assumptions and carefully-crafted, step-by-step reasoning.

Although courses on proof have emerged in the undergraduate curriculum in recent decades, for the most part, mathematicians have developed their conception of proof in settings where their early attempts were questioned: "How did you get from here to here?" or "I believe this, but why is your next statement true?" What then follows is an act of reflection, a reorganization of ideas, and hopefully reasons that "fill the gaps" so a proof can emerge. Mathematicians then live this process throughout their careers.

The case is no different for the "young mathematicians at work" in our classrooms because the development of proof is fostered by having to convince others. If we look at the history of proof across cultures we see evidence for this claim.

In its earliest days, mathematics was often bound up with practical questions. The Egyptians, as well as the Greeks, were concerned with surveying land, designing theater arenas and water tanks, and other practical projects. Thus it was natural to consider mathematical questions related to geometry and trigonometry. In this context, if one could draw a compelling picture or give a convincing description, then that was all the justification that was needed for a mathematical "fact." Sometimes one argued by analogy, or by invoking the gods. The notion that mathematical statements could be *proved* was not yet an idea that existed. There was no standard for the structure of proof—the "rules of the game" had not yet been created (Krantz, 2007).

Ancient mathematicians thought hard though about how to frame a convincing argument. Where would the starting point be? How could one develop a chain of reasoning that would hold together? Thales (640 B.C.E.–546 B.C.E.), Eudoxus (408 B.C.E.–355 B.C.E.), and Theaetetus of Athens (417 B.C.E.–369 B.C.E.) formulated theorems, and Thales proved some of these theorems in geometry (Krantz, 2007).

A **theorem** is the mathematician's formal statement of an accepted fact or truth. An **axiom** or **postulate** is a proposition that is not proved but considered to be obvious, or self-evident. Therefore, its truth is taken for granted, and serves as a starting point for deducing and inferring other truths. Unlike theorems, axioms cannot be derived by principles of deduction, nor are they demonstrable by mathematical proofs, simply because they are starting points; there is nothing else from which they logically follow. Otherwise, they would be classified as theorems. The commutative, associative, and distributive properties are examples of axioms.

It was Euclid of Alexandria who first formalized the way that we now think about proof in mathematics. He built arguments with a chain of reasoning, step-by-step, starting with definitions, then axioms, then theorems (Krantz, 2007).

Today's mathematicians craft proofs using a variety of techniques, such as deduction (the approach used by Euclid), induction (showing how to start and also how to increase one at a time), contradiction (showing that if something isn't true, contradictions arise), and exhaustion (checking all cases). Many reason with representations like Archimedes did. And still others use computers to examine all cases. No matter what form of proof is used, two ingredients are critical: (1) the language and definitions must be clear (no ambiguity), and (2) each statement must follow logically from information previously established using mathematically accepted *rules of inference*.

A basic rule of inference, first analyzed in abstract form by Aristotle, is *modus ponendo ponens* (usually abbreviated *modus ponens*). This rule of logic says that if we know that A implies B, and if we know A, then we may conclude B. One way to build a proof is to find a sequence of statements linked together by *modus ponens*. Many deductive proofs are built up this way, starting with basic assumptions and definitions followed by applications of *modus ponens* or other related deductive rules.

A second basic rule of inference is *universal generalization*. To find out if something is true mathematicians often begin by looking at examples. But checking examples isn't usually enough to see whether something is always true, for there may be many, even infinite cases. However, if an example checks out, and if we can examine the example thoroughly to see that no special assumptions were used in the reasoning that would limit the approach to all the cases, then universal generalization allows mathematicians to claim the result *for all*.

A Landscape of Learning for Proof

At first, when asked to justify their thinking, young children usually say they know they are right because they have checked their work. They consider only themselves as the one who needs to be convinced. When asked how they know something to be true or to be generalizable (that it will work for a set of numbers not just that one case), they say they have tried it with 2 or 3 more examples, and it worked for those numbers, too.

On their poster, they assume just showing their work is sufficient as a "proof," as they are convinced they are right and what they did is shown! In a nutshell, a request to "prove your thinking" or "make a poster to convince us" gets interpreted by children at this point in their development as "show your work." Figure 8.1 is an example. Although the strategy reflected on the poster makes use of partial products, there is no attempt made to explain and justify each step to an audience.

The more children are asked to write arguments to convince others, and to partake in gallery walks to review and write reviewers' comments on the posters displayed, the more they begin to realize that just showing one's work is insufficient to convince their peers. They frequently get comments from their peers, in fact, such as, "I don't know what you did," or "I understand the first part, but then I got confused." The gallery walk with its review process eventually causes these students to begin to consider their audience. Thus, rather than only showing what they did, they begin notating on their posters what they want their audience to notice, and they begin to offer a narrative of their process as an explanation. See Figure 8.2, where 2 third graders, May and Rafe, provide a key and an explanation to help their audience understand what they did.

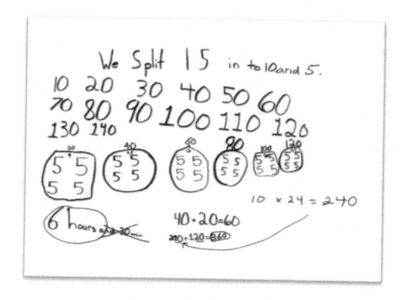

Figure 8.1
A poster of work to justify that a turkey (24 lb. @ 15 min. per lb.) will take 6 hours to
cook

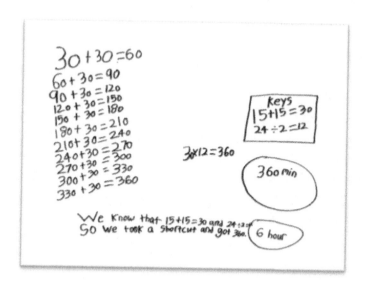

Figure 8.2
A Beginning Narrative and a Key for the Audience

Once children see that the standard for a proof is convincing other people that their thinking makes sense, they add more and more detail into their narratives. Lucy Calkins (1986), in discussing the development of narrative writing, describes early attempts as bed-to-bed stories. Here is an example [Note: the text has been rewritten for readability].

> *I woke up and got dressed and brushed my teeth. I ate my breakfast and then got on the school bus. On the bus I sat with Rafael and when we got to school we played in the playground. Then Mrs. Slater had us write stories and do math. We had pizza for lunch and afterwards we played in the playground some more. Then we did art and science. When the bus came Rafael and I sat together again. When I got home, my mom said, "Guess what? We are having pizza for dinner." I was happy, and then I went to bed.*

Children's narrative writing in mathematics early on is quite similar. It is usually a detailed description or *retelling* of their approaches in solving a problem. This is an important step in learning to articulate one's reasoning, and in the early grades it often marks the onset of an awareness of one's own reasoning, as well as the need to convince others. Children may write something like, "At first we did this, but it didn't work so we tried that, and then we added it all up and we found our answer." They retell the story of exactly what they did as they worked on the problem, step-by-step.

Although such writing might develop language and help students focus on clarity, it is still only an explanation of what was done and should not be confused with the writing of a viable argument (as specified in the CCSS Standards of Mathematical Practice). It is not yet a proof. The main problem with the commonly-used directives in elementary classrooms, "put in words, pictures and symbols for me what you did" or "show your work and explain your thinking" is that these directives keep children at this early stage of development. They do not foster growth in proof-making because providing proof to a community requires a reorganization of ideas into a chain of logically connected statements, which involves *analysis and resequencing of a process* in search of a *convincing chain of reasoning*, rather than a retelling of what was done. To do this requires that learners not only take the perspective of the audience, but that they provide a justification to the audience that they are right—they need to think about the thinking! The ability to do this is a major turning point in development and it needs to be consciously fostered as we confer. A graphic of the fuller Landscape of Learning for proof is provided in Figure 8.3. The bottom third of the graphic represents the prior discussion—the early development of proof. Let's go back to the classroom to see how conferrals can support development along it.

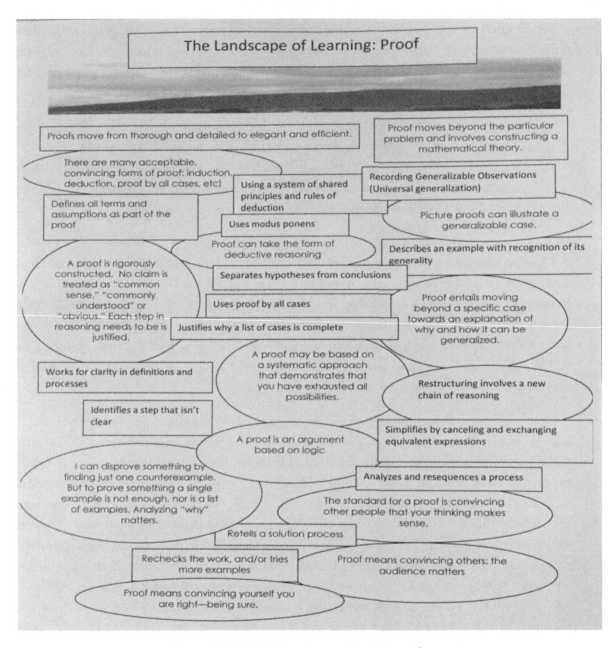

Figure 8.3: The Development of Proof[2]

[2] This version is a modification by the author of an original previously-published version for teachers in Imm, Fosnot, Dolk, Jacob, and Stylianou (2012). *Learning to Support Young Mathematicians at Work* Portsmouth NH: Heinemann. Adapted with permission.

Conferring to Support this Development

Leah has invited her students to investigate possible two-color farm fences that can be used in the making of a length of 32. Earlier in the week the children had used Cuisenaire Rods to model the problem using the following colored lengths: light green (length 3), purple (length 4), dark green (length 6), and brown (length 8). Now they are working to represent their ideas on an open number line, and to prepare a poster for a gallery walk.

Harry and Margarita have been working with 3s and 6s, and they don't think it is possible to build 32. On their poster they have written:

> *First we tried all 3s but that didn't work since 3+3+3+3+3+3+3+3+3+3 = 30, and we know 30 is too little but if we do 3 more we get more than 32. So next we tried one 6 and more 3s but that still didn't work. We tried using two and three 6s but that didn't work either. So it is impossible.*

Leah notes that on their poster Harry and Margarita are just retelling what they did. Although they are listing the possibilities they have tried and have provided reasons for their next move, they have not yet considered if all possibilities have been tried. Nor, have they made an attempt to justify to others that all possibilities have been considered—a critical piece in structuring the relationships sufficiently to craft a compact proof.

Sonia and Alice are sitting at the same table across from them and they are also working on 3s and 6s. They have started the same way, adding up 3s, but they have used the open number line to model their strategy, and when they use 6s they realize that it is the same as adding 3s, just 2 at a time.

Leah sits to confer with the group of four together. She begins with an invitation and asks for clarification, "How is it going? I see that the four of you are trying out the threes and the sixes, and it seems you agree that they don't work, but I think your reasons why are different. Tell me more about your thinking so I can see if I understand your arguments."

Harry and Margarita respond first, by reading what they have written on their poster. Leah queries further, for clarification on their purpose, "So is the intent of your argument to convince everyone that using 3 or 6 is not possible?" Both agree that this is the intent. Leah decides that later in the conversation she will up the ante and challenge. First though, she celebrates what they are trying to do, "That's a great idea to make that a focus. Proving that something is impossible is a cool idea. Will you continue like this with the other colors, too?"

Margarita responds, affirmatively, pleased that Leah is interested and understands their approach, "Yes, we are going to check the other ones, too. Then we'll know which ones work, and which ones don't."

"Wow, you are really working like mathematicians on this!"

Leah continues initiating them into the community of mathematicians and taking her role as mentor seriously, "Many adult mathematicians use this way of proving things, too. And I bet you didn't even know that...you invented it yourselves! Wow!"

Margarita and Harry beam with obvious pride at the fact that they have invented something adult mathematicians use. Leah continues, "Adult mathematicians call an argument like this, 'proof by exhaustion!' They try every possibility until they know for certain they have tried them all. Then they know they are right, and they publish their results to convince others. They call it proof by exhaustion because they have exhausted every possibility; there are no more left to test." Now Leah challenges, "So one of things that will be important for you to consider as you write your proof is how you know you have tried all the possibilities. During our gallery walk I can imagine that someone might put that question on a sticky note for you, 'How do you know there aren't more possibilities?' How will you convince your audience that there are no more?"

"I think there are more ways, too. I bet there are a lot of ways!" Harry exclaims. "I bet they also call it that because they are exhausted when they are done!"

Leah smiles at Harry's humor and decides this is the moment to bring Sonia and Alice into the conversation. "What are your thoughts on this question, girls? You are working on the same two colors and I can see you agree with Harry and Margarita—that it is not possible to do it with these two colors. Have you found more possibilities with these colors? Are there more possibilities that Harry and Margarita need to consider before they can conclude it is impossible?"

"There are more ways," Sonia offers. "You only tried some ways with 6. Did you try four 6s, or five 6s? You could keep going like that. But, we know they won't work. We showed that on our number line. See?" she turns and pushes her poster forward to show what she and Alice have written. As she does, she also puts forth a powerful piece of modus ponens reasoning, "If you use 6s, it's the same as using two 3s, so if you know it doesn't work with threes, it can't work with sixes either. So, light green and dark green won't work together. It's the same as just using threes and we know that doesn't work."

"Oh yeah…." Harry smiles with obvious delight, and relief. "That's a good idea. Now we don't have to keep trying lots and lots of ways. We won't get exhausted!"

Leah chuckles again at Harry's humor, and then makes use of it as she comments, "That is just what makes crafting a proof so much fun! Right? You keep trying to make it crisper and crisper, cleaner and clearer until it is elegant! What a gorgeous piece you will have here when you finish. Let me make sure I understand what you are thinking about doing next, because I need to move on to confer with some other kids."

Because Leah is about to move to another group to confer, she wants to frame the direction that this group is now heading. "So you are now saying you tried 3, and you have an argument on your poster already as to why it doesn't work. Then you are saying: if 3 rods don't work, 6 can't work either because 6 equals two 3s. Will this reasoning work with the 4 and 8 as well? Maybe you might want to try those two colors next? If you do, let me know what happens. Ok? This is very exciting!"

What is Revealed

As we reflect on Leah's conferral, what has been revealed? First, the conferral has been instrumental in fostering a movement away from just a retelling of what the children have done, to the *restructuring of a proof with a new chain of reasoning,* which in this case is more direct. The two pairs have been introduced to "proof by exhaustion" and are building an argument with a chain of reasoning based on *modus ponens.*

The chain of reasoning now being used is also based on another important strategy: *treating expressions as interchangeable equivalent objects;* 6 can be exchanged for two 3s. The power of these ideas is that the proof is becoming tighter, crisper and more convincing. Leah's hope as she leaves is that the children will explore the 4s and the 8s next and come to realize that since 8s work, 4s will work as an 8 rod can be exchanged for two 4s. The only possibilities left to explore then will be the remaining combinations: 8 with 6 or 3; and 4 with 6 or 3. But because of the first steps in their new proof, these possibilities can be narrowed down, accordingly.

Helpful Supports

When we sit to confer with students as they write up viable arguments, several types of questions can be helpful. I often start with, "What do you want to convince your audience of?" and then I move to something like, "How will you convince them?" With children who are not considering the perspective of an audience, I might ask, "What do you think your friends will need to know to be convinced?" And then, "What are your thoughts on how to do this? How will you begin?"

As students get older and have had several years of experience with math workshop, including postering and gallery walks, they are quite comfortable writing for a math audience. In fact, they have often internalized the earlier questions and already are asking themselves those questions. So now my questions shift to, "What are your assumptions, where will you start, do you need to define anything for your audience, what form of proof are you considering?"

Before the gallery walk, I tell children, "Step back and reflect on your argument. Ask yourself if there is anything else your audience will need to know. Is there anything you want to emphasize, highlight, or make sure they notice? Sometimes I take on the role of a pretend reviewer and do a little minilesson on the review process.

At the end of the gallery walk, children collect their posters and examine the comments they got from reviewers. As they read through them, I move around and confer again, this time asking things like, "What notes did you get from your reviewers? What did their comments tell you that might be important? In light of the comments you got, how do you plan to revise your work? Did the argument you made seem to convince them? Did they point out any places in your chain of reasoning that had holes? Were there any places where you lost your readers, where you might need to add more detail because they didn't seem to understand what you meant?" Or, "Now that you have had time to reflect on what other mathematicians in this community did, have you thought about any revisions you want to make?" And then of course, children need ample time to revise.

Summing Up

Mathematics writing in our elementary classrooms has been so misunderstood. If we are to take seriously the CCSS Standard of Mathematical Practice: read and write a viable argument, we will need to provide ample opportunities in our classrooms for children to write and read arguments, examine one another's logic and chain of reasoning, and allow for revision.

Learning to write a mathematical argument takes time and goes through a "landscape" of development. Our goal is to encourage our children to see themselves as thinkers, as Halmos said (in the epigraph to this chapter), "Don't just read it; fight it! Ask your own questions, look for your own examples, and discover your own proofs. Is the hypothesis necessary? Is the converse true? What happens in the classical special case? What about the degenerate cases? Where does the proof use the hypothesis?" Our job as mentors is to foster this type of thinking.

Chapter Nine

* * *

Documenting the Learning

You cannot step twice into the same stream. For as you are stepping in, other waters are ever flowing.

—Heraclitus

Static versus Dynamic Assessment

Assessment should guide teaching. It should be continuous and provide information about the "zone of proximal development" (Vygotsky 1978). To do so, it needs to foresee where and how one can anticipate that which is just coming into view in the distance (Streefland 1985). It needs to capture genuine mathematizing: children's strategies, their ways of modeling realistic problems, and their understanding of key mathematical ideas. Bottom line, it needs to capture where the child is on the landscape of learning—where she has been, what her struggles are, and where she is going: it must be dynamic (Fosnot and Dolk 2001; van den Heuvel-Panhuizen 1996).

Most forms of assessment are not dynamic or continuous; they are static and discrete. Even when called "formative" assessments, they are usually isolated items on a written test. Tests designed this way, by their very nature, can only pick up information about how a child performs on them, on that day, in that moment in time; and, what is picked up needs to be understood as dependent on the way the item is crafted. Static assessments like these are usually designed to determine what a child cannot do, rather than what he can do (de Lange

1992).

When Vygotsky (1978) wrote about the "zone of proximal development" he was referring to the zone in which a child was capable of learning as he worked with a knowledgeable other. Knowledge is fluid and complex. Some days we feel sharp: we remember details and do things easily; on other days these very same things may seem more elusive. Discussion with a peer can sometimes jog the memory or provide insights we wouldn't have had alone. When provided with time to revise and edit, our thinking also changes and reflects better our growing and changing capabilities.

Documenting During Conferrals

As we converse with children in conferrals, we are provided with powerful moments to assess dynamically. We get to hear about children's intended goals, the strategies they are trying and want to try, and in general the ways in which they are mathematizing their lives. We get to see which strategies they are comfortable with, and which are just a bit out of reach at the present moment. The human side of learning comes into view as we listen: we get to witness children's ideas, their wonderments, their excitements, and their puzzlements. We see them elated and frustrated. We get to understand them as young mathematicians. Listening intently to children as we converse with them, allows us to better understand their journeys along the landscape of learning—what landmarks of development they have passed, what landmarks are nearby, and what is just out of reach but on their near horizons.

In previous chapters we explored how the landscapes of learning can be useful as powerful frameworks in conferrals, helping teachers know what to celebrate, what to "get under" and support, and how to up the ante and challenge. As we confer, all of this can be documented to produce a more dynamic picture (in contrast to a static, discrete one) of the mathematical development of a child and so the landscapes become useful tools again—this time for documentation of learning.

Years ago, when I started Mathematics in the City, we did all our documentation during conferrals with pencil and paper. When conferring, teachers would bring clipboards, notepaper, and/or spreadsheets. Some used a rolodex of index cards—one card for each child. They would use these for anecdotal records—descriptive, detailed notes about what they observed during the conferral, including analysis of the work sample, and the date. Later the child's work sample would be copied and stapled to the notes and these would be placed in a student's portfolio. The portfolios would then be used as evidence of learning or as discussion points during parent/teacher conferences. Over the course of the year, the accumulated notes and work samples provided evidence of growth and development over time. When spreadsheets were used, teachers would list children's names, the date of the conferral, and the focus of the conferral. These served as helpful notes to remember whom they had conferred with on each day, and what the focus of each had been. A sample spreadsheet of the type we used is provided in Figure 9.1. The associated children's work is shown in Figure 9.2.

Over time, many of the teachers we worked with also began to find the graphics of the landscapes from the CFLM units helpful as documentation tools during a conferral. Using highlighters, they would color in the big ideas, strategies, and the models they saw evidence of children using and understanding. On the back they would list the dates of the conferrals, and add any additional notes they found helpful to remember for future conferrals.

They made copies of each needed landscape (depending on the grade) for each child in their class. A green highlighter was used for landmark strategies children used frequently and had clearly mastered (or passed). A yellow highlighter was used for landmarks children were attempting to use, which were still considered to be fragile. Yellow meant review, meaning that teachers would keep these landmarks in mind when conferring and continue to support development of them. Figures of previously published landscapes in various CFLM units, discussed in this book, are available for your use as full page graphics in Figures 9.3-9.5. More detailed information on each landscape can be found within each unit, as well as on P2S2: a personalized professional support system™. For information on this online support system, go to: **www.NewPerspectivesOnline.net.**

Pitfalls

Documenting with paper and pencil and organizing records in folders takes a lot of time. It is also critical when conferring to be listening intently and engaging actively in a conversation. Record-keeping can get in the way of a good conferral as it can be a distractor to both the teacher and the children. Imagine having a conversation with a friend while trying to take notes on the focus of the conversation and the ideas being discussed. This one act can immediately change the flow of the conversation.

I've watched teachers as they try to document during conferrals and I've noticed that while their intentions may be good ones, many teaching moments get missed because they are focused more on assessing than on acting in the moment. I've even wondered if their focus on assessment is based on the idea that they will use their records at another point in time, make homogeneous groups, and teach directly to what they think those learners need—all under the imposed purposes of differentiation and intervention. Sadly, the moments when the teaching would have been powerful were missed.

For these reasons I personally take no notes when conferring. I've tried, and simply cannot do it. I need to stay alert to every word, glance, and bodily gesture of the children I'm working with in order to confer well. I jot down my notes as I walk away and I use my cell phone to quickly take a picture of the work sample we were discussing.

Digital Tools that Can Be Helpful

Today, digital technology provides more efficient, less cumbersome ways of record-keeping. In 2015 we developed a web-based app for documenting, which most of the teachers we currently work with now use. The app makes use of the landscape graphics and teachers set up their record-keeping on the app by entering the names of all the children in their class. Because the app is web-based it is available for use on tablets, iPads, cellphones and desktops. A set of appropriate landscapes is provided under each child's name. The glossary of the terms on each landscape is built-in so that a tap on a landmark on the landscape brings up the definition.

Photos and short video clips are easily attached to the landmarks and saved, and then the landmark is highlighted in green (evidence of solid understanding) or yellow (fragile, attempting to use, need to review). Anecdotal records can also be added in text boxes. Dates of entries are automatically produced by the app. And the records go with the child as he progresses through the grades, just as all school records do. The app includes downloadable formative assessments as well.

I find this tool makes documenting less intrusive to the conversation. Personally, since I'm not very good at multitasking, even when using this tool, I do so when I walk away so I can give 100% of my attention to the learners in front of me when conferring and respond in the moment. I want to make each moment matter and I can't do that while taking notes.

For more information on the assessment app, use the QR Code provided here:

Or go to:

www.NewPerspectivesOnAssessment.com

Summing Up

Documenting learning needs to be done dynamically, not statically. As Heraclitus says in the epigraph, "You cannot step twice into the same stream. For as you are stepping in, other waters are ever flowing." Learning is complex and fluid like the stream—ideas and strategies develop over time and through interactions with others. As we confer we have opportunities to assess dynamically by capturing where a child is on the landscape, where she has been, and what is coming into view.

There are many ways to do this, taking notes with paper and pencil, using spreadsheets, and taking photos of work samples. Even the landscape graphics themselves can be useful. Today, digital technology also affords tools that may be easier to use and be less intrusive to the conversations we have with our young mathematicians at work. Using them may help to make the moments matter.

CONFERENCE NOTES			
Child's Name	Date	Analysis of Math Work	On the Near Horizon
Scarlett and Cassandra

(Work sample is shown in Figure 9.2; the conferral is in Chapter 2) | 11/15 | Cooking the Turkey

CFLM unit, The Big Dinner

Repeated addition, groups can be regrouped | Doubling and halving,

equivalence of expressions, associative property |
| Marlin, Kenneth, and Sam | 11/15 | Cooking the Turkey

CFLM unit, The Big Dinner

Skip counting, ratio thinking | Doubling, groups can be

regrouped,

ratio table model |
| Ese and Harry | 11/15 | Cooking the Turkey

CFLM unit, The Big Dinner

Skip counting, groups can be regrouped, unitizing | Quadrupling and quartering

Take audience into

consideration when writing

a proof |
| **Figure 9.1**
A Sample Spreadsheet for Conferrals | | | |

Figure 9.2
Samples of Work for the Children Mentioned in Figure 9.1

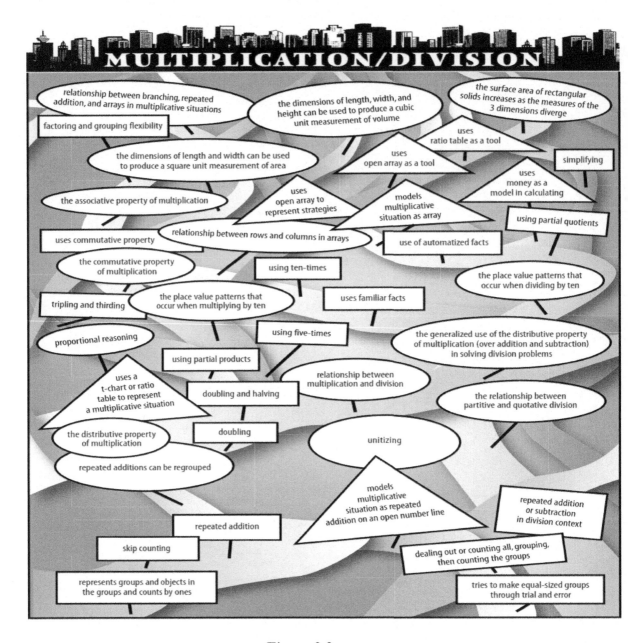

Figure 9.3
The Multiplication Landscape[3]

---

[3] This landscape is from Fosnot, C.T. (2007) *Contexts for Learning Mathematics*. Portsmouth NH: Heinemann. Published with permission.

Figure 9.4
The Early Number Sense, Addition and Subtraction Landscape[4]

[4] This landscape is from Fosnot, C.T. (2007) *Contexts for Learning Mathematics*. Portsmouth NH: Heinemann. Published with permission.

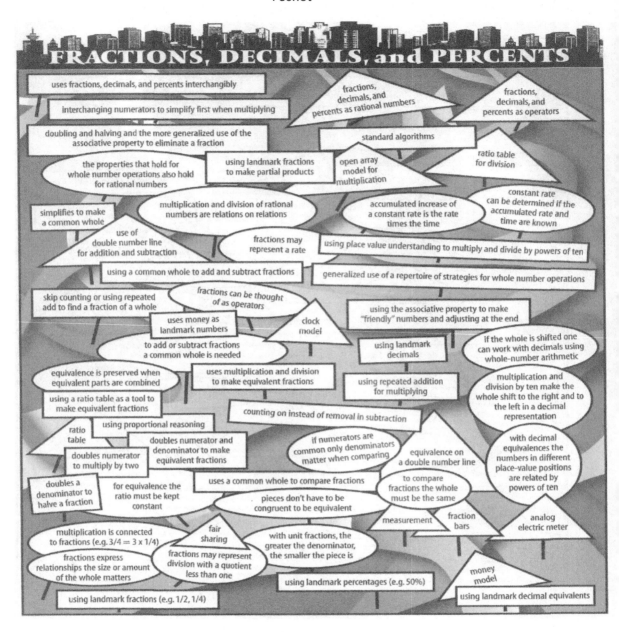

Figure 9.5
The Fraction Landscape[5]

[5] This landscape is from Fosnot, C.T. (2007) *Contexts for Learning Mathematics*. Portsmouth NH: Heinemann. Published with permission.

Chapter Ten

* * *

A Chapter for Coaches: Helping Teachers to Question

Organizations change when their members can identify their most deeply ingrained assumptions, then unearth a shared picture of the future and go after it together.

—Peter Senge, The Fifth Discipline

Most of us (teachers, administrators, teacher educators, and math coaches alike) are products of an educational system that we are now being asked to change. When I was in elementary school most of my math instruction was about procedures and why they worked. My teachers explained concepts such as place value and the properties of operations; then showed me algorithms for computation based on these concepts and had me practice them. Formulas were introduced with explanations of how they had been derived, and I was then asked to apply them in word problems. Calculations were all done with paper and pencil and my job as an elementary school student was to learn to do them proficiently—like a human calculator. To wit, arithmetic was the focus.

Even in my later mathematics courses, in algebra and calculus, I witnessed professors filling chalkboards with derivations of procedures and their proofs. My job as a student was to apply what they had explained in rather routine problems after learning the procedures. I even learned later when I became a college professor myself that some departments of mathematics included "use of the chalkboard" as one of their criteria in evaluating professors for tenure!

Times have certainly changed. Most calculations are done today with hand-held devices such as calculators, cell-phones, wristwatches, and tablets. When the children in our elementary classes reach adulthood, most likely they will be wearing devices like google glasses and/or have implants with calculating tools. Even without these, they will simply ask Siri or Cortana for the answer.

Because the world is changing so rapidly, the basics have shifted away from practicing algorithms, towards the development of numeracy and the deeper understanding of mathematics. It's not important that we perform all calculations ourselves, but we better know what to tell digital tools to do, and be able to recognize whether the answers we get are reasonable, or not.

Most high paying jobs of the future (for example, computer engineers, software developers, biomedical technology engineers, aerospace engineers and astrobiologists, etc.) will require a substantial amount of mathematics. Thus, building a foundation for higher mathematics in the elementary school is important in order to keep career options for our children open.

Arithmetic can be taught through explanation and practice because algorithms do not require thinking: they are just behaviors, steps to be performed sequentially and flawlessly regardless of the numbers. With enough practice and feedback, humans can be taught to perform them. The problem however is that mathematics and numeracy (in contrast to arithmetic) require thinking, not just routinized behaviors.

Today in our classrooms, children are expected to be young mathematicians at work involved in mathematical inquiries. Problems are used to *generate* mathematics, in contrast to the application of previously learned procedures—as was the case when I was in elementary school. The CCSS Standards of Mathematical Practice require that we engage children in the *doing* of mathematics. This fact alone has made effective questioning and conferring (mentoring) critical to good teaching. Teachers are no longer judged on their use of the chalkboard or on effective communication, but on their ability to engage children in mathematical thinking, and to question and mentor effectively.

Yet, it is unlikely that most of us have experienced teachers who did this with us. How are teachers supposed to know what it really means to *do* mathematics, and to mentor and confer with our young mathematicians effectively, when it is unlikely that we have experienced it ourselves?

The Landscape: Changing the Way We Question

Precisely because most of our personal experiences as learners have been with teachers who explained procedures, requested repeated practice of them, and then gave feedback, as we attempt to change our pedagogy it is often difficult for us to trust that learners could ever generate mathematical ideas and strategies on their own. Sometimes teachers believe this so strongly, they ask almost no questions at all.

If, as coaches, we do "demo lessons" to model questioning for teachers, or suggest to them that asking questions, rather than explaining, might get learners more engaged, we may see more questions used, but usually the subsequent questions that get asked are for motivational purposes, keeping learners attentive, rather than for promoting deeper thinking. Sometimes the questions we see being asked are even designed for one word answers—answers the teacher wants to hear. For example, this is the dialogue I heard in a 4th grade classroom one day:

Teacher: And what is this part of the rectangle called?... Juan?

Juan: The area.

Teacher: The area. Right. And how do we get the area?... Harry?

Harry: Length times... width?

Teacher: Excellent. Length times width. And how do I write that? …. Maria?

Maria: l x w = A.

Teacher: Good job. I can see you are all paying attention and thinking today. So now I have some problems for you to work on. In some of the problems you are told one dimension and the area, and you have to figure out the other dimension. In others you are told the length and the width, and you need to figure out the area. Work with a partner, and I'll come around and confer to help.

After everyone was settled and working, the teacher moved around the room then sat with a pair to confer. The two children were just multiplying the two numbers given, whether they were both dimensions of the rectangle, or not.

Teacher: Why are you multiplying?

Child 1: Because you told us to. You said l x w = A

Teacher: That's the formula for area. You already know the area. It says 36 sq. ft. here. See how it says square feet? That means the 36 is the area of this rectangle. You also know the length; it shows it here on the picture. It is 9 ft. What don't you know?

Child 2: The answer?

Teacher: Right. I know, but what is this dimension called?

Child 1: The width?

Teacher: Excellent! Yes, it is the width. So you know the length, I'll write 9, times…a box, because we don't know that piece of the problem…that's the width, …equals… 36 square ft.

On the paper is now written: 9 x □ *= 36 sq. ft.*

Teacher: So how do we find out what is in the box? 9 times "what" equals 36?

Child 2: Four. 9 x 4 = 36.

Teacher: Four what?

Child 2: Four feet?

Teacher: Yes. Excellent. So 4 ft. is the width. Keep working like this, ok? Think about what you know and don't know. I need to go confer with some other kids now, but I'll check back with you later.

The problem this teacher is having is not that she needs to ask questions instead of explaining. She is actually asking a lot of questions. The problem is that the questions she is asking are not conducive to thinking deeply. She thinks she is conferring, but really she is just moving around the room to make sure everyone is doing the assignment correctly. She has been told her role is to be a facilitator, so she questions, but underlying this behavior is a belief system.

Let's take a look at a Landscape of Learning on Teacher Change, in particular one on questioning and conferring. See Figure 10.1. Note that her strategies and ideas about questions are near the bottom of the landscape. This teacher still believes mathematics is about procedures, labels, formulae, and equations—all things she perhaps use to transmit. These are listed as year-end objectives on her curriculum and she is covering them by teaching directly to them as she has always done, but now she does so by asking questions to motivate and keep students engaged, rather than just telling. Her questions are used to generate the recall of mathematical facts or vocabulary and are largely focused on mathematical procedures because these are the things she thinks her students need to know. She is questioning to get her learners to think about them.

In the ovals just above that section of the landscape, there are two big ideas this teacher will need to construct to make any further progress in learning to question more powerfully: 1) Teaching is about development; 2) Questioning can foster development. These at first glance may seem like easy shifts. As coaches, we might think that our focus should just be to use a cognitive, or a content-based, coaching model. The former would suggest we foster reflection on the purpose of the teacher's questions to get at her belief system; the latter would suggest we start with a discussion about the mathematics in the activity.

Although both approaches have some benefits, neither is likely to be powerful enough to foster the kind of substantial cognitive reorganization and change in behavior that is needed. The required shifts at this juncture are major: they require earlier ideas to actually be negated, and the new ideas are dependent upon the development of a complex network of several interrelated pathways.

Looking at Change through the Lens of Stages

Many years ago, Paul Ammon (1993), a researcher and head of the Developmental Teacher Education program at UC Berkeley, completed a large study on teachers' beliefs about learning and teaching. He interviewed several teachers from his program over several years, analyzed their teaching logs, lesson plans, and journals, and performed several case studies. He characterized his results as a stage theory and delineated 5 stages of growth.

It may be helpful to overlay this framework over the landscape to better understand the types of shifts in beliefs that are required as teachers move along the landscape. A brief summary follows on page 107.

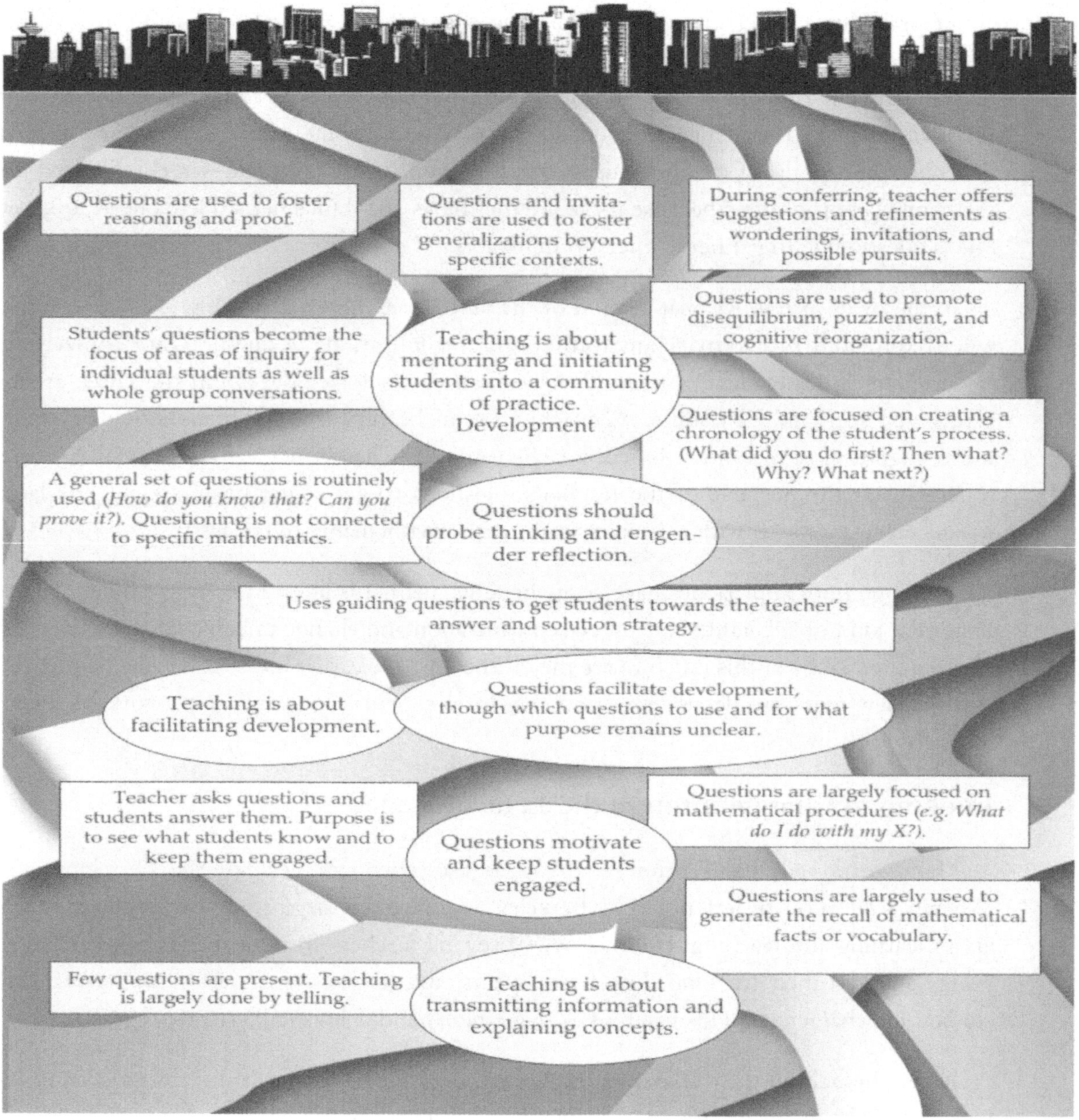

Figure 10.1
Teacher Change: Questioning and Conferring[6]

[6] This landscape is from Imm, Fosnot, Dolk, Jacob and Stylianou, (2012). *Learning to Support Young Mathematicians at Work*. Portsmouth: NH: Heinemann. Published with permission.

Level One:

- *Learning*: Acquisition of specific facts, rules, and attitudes, learned by exposure

- *Teaching*: Show and tell students what they need to know

Level Two:

- *Learning*: Acquisition of skills, formulas, and procedures, learned by imitation, practice, and reinforcement

- *Teaching*: Engage students in activities to assess what they can and can't do, teach what they need to know, and provide feedback as they work to reinforce and strengthen desired behavior

Level Three:

- *Learning*: Acquisition of skills and concepts, learned by discovery of the "correct" (usually the teacher's) understanding

- *Teaching*: Support active discovery or "hands-on" learning to induce "correct" understandings

Level Four:

- *Learning*: Attainment of *an* understanding of some content (a change in an interpretation or strategy), learned by hearing and thinking about others' ideas

- *Teaching*: Promote discourse and reflection

Level Five:

- *Learning*: Progressive development that affects content understandings and reasoning in general, learned by cognitive reconstruction

- *Teaching*: Teach people to think by fostering disequilibrium and puzzlement, discourse, reflection, and argumentation

The teacher we have been studying in the prior transcript is at Ammon's Level Two. She is asking questions, most likely because she knows that is expected of her, but she still believes in reinforcement. Note how she keeps saying, "excellent" when she hears the answer she wants. She sees no difference between questions that demand one word answers and those that require much deeper thinking because to her mathematics is about the names, formulas, and procedures she sees as correct—they are the intended goals of her instruction.

Note the difference in Levels Three and Four. At Level Three, learning is still viewed as a list of correct understandings—intended outcomes of activities to produce things from the list of objectives (most likely a list of skills and concepts) that the teacher wants the children to know. At Level Three emphasis turns to understanding and a teacher's pedagogy may have shifted to the use of active learning using a discovery model to achieve it, but this is not a mentoring model. At Level Three the teacher may have students working on problems and she is likely moving around and conferring with them as they work. She perhaps will promote discovery more than the teacher in the prior transcript, but she will struggle with what to ask, just as Eileen did in Chapter One. The reason is because the intended goals of the learning have not changed. They are still a list of skills and concepts seen as outcomes of the activity. Teachers at Level Three may even talk about learner construction. They say things like, "I know my children need to construct their own understanding. I want them to understand the concepts, but I just don't know what to ask to help them." But between the lines, they are saying "My children should discover what I intend. To facilitate their learning, I should ask questions to guide them to my intended objectives and understanding and I don't know what to ask to make that happen."

Teachers can stay at the middle part of the Landscape of Learning for a very long time. They often get stuck there, as we saw with Eileen in Chapter one. Some get there and never leave. There are a variety of reasons for this immobility.

First, a great deal needs to be learned about the development of the content they are required to reach by the end of the year. To reach "can multiply numbers (2 digit by 2-digit) using place value and properties of operations" by the end of the year, teachers need to deeply understand the *progressive development* of this content (for example, the Landscape of Learning described in Chapter Three.) But more, they need to learn how to *consciously support* this development throughout the year.

Levels Four and Five require a shift in goals—a complete shift in the way learning is understood. Learning is no longer looked at as a list of skills and concepts; it is looked at as fostering the growth and development of a young mathematician. At Level Three, an outcome such as "can multiply numbers (2 digit by 2-digit) using place value and properties of operations" is seen as the goal of an activity, or a section of a text or unit to be covered in a short period of time.

In contrast, at Level Four the learning outcome of the same activity (or activities) is seen as *an* understanding of *some* content resulting from reasoning about it. What learners do in an activity is seen as *their interpretation of the content objective at this moment in their development.* Thus, "can multiply numbers (2 digit by 2-digit) using place value and properties of operations" is now viewed as a year-end objective resulting from a gradual process of development over the course of the year, not as an intended goal of a unit of study or a sequence of activities. This means that, during the activities, conversation and reflection become critical because these processes promote development. All we can consciously work to promote is development, which means the outcome of an activity will be different for each learner.

At Level Five learning is understood as progressive development. Teachers support development through *the sequences of investigations they use, the constraints they build into the contexts, and as they confer.* They understand that they are working with young mathematicians at work and they are teaching them to think. The thinking they foster will have ramifications for all learning because they are helping the children in their care build meaning and to seriously engage in the standards of mathematical practice. They are mentoring young mathematicians at work and making the moments while conferring matter.

Supporting and Fostering Change

Let me be clear that I am not blaming teachers for getting stuck in the middle of the landscape (Figure 10.1), for feeling like they don't know what to ask when they are conferring. The problems are far more systemic for teachers to be the ones blamed. The problems are endemic to the structures surrounding the teachers, which often work to stunt growth and hinder the changes needed for the future.

For example, I've seen some districts (as they work to align with CCSS or state year-end objectives) employ teachers during the summer to design activities for the intended outcomes. Then a pacing calendar is used to place the teacher-designed activities at specific times of the year. The intentions are meant well, but the teachers have not been provided with the necessary understanding of development to enable them to design progressive developmental sequences (that in itself requires a very long journey of professional learning), so they design activities, and just placing the activities at a point in the year with pacing calendars suggests that these activities are isolated and have intended learning outcomes. This practice promotes Level Two thinking.

Other districts just adopt new textbooks, and most of the ones currently on the market are designed at Level Two, or Three. They consist of a host of hands-on or paper/pencil activities, each with intended outcomes. Some prescribe activities and/or workbook pages and give teachers directions for each to assess what children can and can't do. Explanations are provided as ways to teach the intended outcome, and directions are given as to how to provide feedback to reinforce and produce correct behavior—Level Two.

Others provide activities to induce "correct" understandings through discovery—Level Three. A few make some attempt to provide teachers with information on some sample alternative strategies children might give and the kinds of discussions that might occur (at least an attempt at Level Four), but none make progressive long term development of the content transparent to teachers—Level Five. Most instead actually promote the idea that learning is a set of intended skills and concepts that should result from the doing of the activities. That is why I'm describing them as Level Two, or at best Level Three. [Some on the market are so scripted I would even classify them as Level One.]

But, the textbooks that districts adopt are not the only problem. To make matters worse, the current wave of "data-driven" instruction promotes the use of formative assessments to determine "who got the intended learning and who didn't" so that teachers can then teach even more directly to a list of prescribed outcomes, this time with smaller, more homogeneous, groups. Teachers have no time to consider, or learn about, the development of the content, as they are required to spend all of their time labeling, documenting, and prescribing.

The amount of assessment data being accumulated in schools is rising to an astronomical level with little effect on real learning. According to a recent report by the Brown Center on Education Policy at the Brookings Institution (Chingos, 2012), the United States spends upwards of roughly $1.7 billion on assessments per state, per year, and the amount will continue to rise as the government moves to an emphasis on formative assessments and the Common Core State Standards. Sometimes, in my darkest days, I think all we are now promoting in our schools is assessment, scoring, and teaching to tests—in other words, test prep. No amount of coaching, even when math content and developmental trajectories are part of the discussion, will likely be impactful enough to create the climate for districts to restructure their current practices.

After many years directing Mathematics in the City and having opportunities to witness firsthand the multifaceted, complex pathways needed for change in math education if we are to seriously meet the challenges of the future, I have come to believe that a massive multi-pronged approach is needed—and even then the journey will be a long one. In 2010, I retired from CCNY early so I could focus my energy in the remaining years of my career on the production of new curriculum and professional development materials for the 21st century, and particularly to include the harnessing of digital technologies in this task.

First and foremost, we need to trust our teachers to grow and we need to put the structures around them that will foster their growth. We talk about how teachers need to learn to trust that children can generate mathematics when rich problems are provided for them to investigate. Yet, we continue to produce more and more prescribed materials, pacing calendars, and assessments for teachers to use because the belief is that teachers won't know what to do unless we tell them.

Just sending teachers to PD workshops or providing coaches will do little with these practices in place. Curriculum needs to be written differently, more as prototypes than a core, and with *a lot of description on development built-in* to allow teachers to come to understand the developmental pathways to get to year-end outcomes and to give them the freedom to use problems from children's lives, run vibrant math workshops, pursue children's inquiries, and, in general, to support mathematical development. Instead of prescribing complete core programs, which only promote coverage and hinder real teaching, prototype units with professional learning built-in should be used to foster growth.

To mentor in powerful ways, to know what to ask, teachers need to be able to analyze children's work and listen, seeing and hearing what the children are trying to do and recognizing that these attempts are children's interpretations of the content—at that point in their development.

When teachers are stuck in the middle of the landscape and struggling with questioning, it can help to confer with them with samples of children's work and the landscapes. As they develop an understanding of mathematical development in relation to the topics they teach, they will become more able to shift their views on learning to one focused on development.

But that will not be sufficient. Teachers also need to know what landmarks of development are on the horizon for those children. They need to be able to answer questions like: where could this strategy that I am seeing go long term; what big ideas are related and could be generalized; what mathematical models might be helpful? They need a fluid sense of the landscape. The landscape is not a linear step-by-step path, but a complex interrelated network of pathways full of strategies, ideas, and models –schemes, structures, and symbolic forms of representation. It is a metaphor of the mind—a graphic of mathematics development, which is complex.

Learning pathways are dependent on many things: the problems learners have worked on previously, the tools they have chosen to model the problems with, the conversations they have been in. As mathematicians we are developing a host of ideas, ways of modeling problems and strategies to attack them with, building a set of exemplar problems, and developing our intuitions. As Devlin says, "We are building a sense of the terrain."

The landscape is the terrain and teachers need to be able to maneuver the terrain with their children. It goes without saying that professional support is critical in this growth process. But what should this support entail? Just sending teachers to PD workshops to learn is Level Two thinking—doing activities over an afternoon or a few days will have little impact on change. This is paramount to doing a few activities with children, each with intended learning goals. And the cost of sustained and frequent PD workshops is prohibitive in cost.

The training of coaches to do "content-based coaching," where the starting point of the discussion is the math in the next activity in the textbook, will not help much either. It will perhaps help teachers use the textbook better, but, let's not confuse that outcome with the needed professional support we are talking about here. Continuing to use Level Two or Three materials and providing coaching around them will not foster the needed changes on the landscape described in this chapter.

Harnessing Technology

Did you notice that in the above paragraph I used the term professional "support" instead of professional learning? The digital technologies of today provide the capacity for on-going, on-demand support in the use of new prototype materials when and where needed. Digital video of exemplary classrooms in action, discussions by the authors of the materials on children's mathematical development with analysis of sample children's work, available conferrals for examination on the precise activities the teachers are about to engage in, forums for questions and discussion can all be made available to teachers at the tips of their fingers. In today's world, the idea of waiting for a scheduled workshop or a weekly visit by a coach for teacher learning to occur is so outdated it is ludicrous.

Today when we want to know something: we google; information is at our fingertips. Imagine a powerful PD platform for teachers to use as support in their own learning—one with a social networking capacity to learn what teachers around the world are doing, but one that also has the ability for a closed system for local professional learning communities.

This is what Maarten Dolk and I have been developing over the last few years: P2S2: a personalized professional support system™. You can take a look at it here.

For more information on P2S2™, use the QR Scan provided here:

Or go to **www.NewPerspectivesOnline.net**

P2S2™ provides video from classrooms for each of the units in *Contexts for Learning Mathematics (CFLM).*[7] Teachers new to math workshop and CFLM can begin with an overview of a unit they are about to teach and the math in it and see video of a math workshop in action. Other more experienced teachers may choose to start with a focus on deepening their understanding of the related landscape, or questioning, or planning math congresses. The platform also provides generic modules (not specific to CFLM) on number strings and representation, conferring, and opportunities for teachers to deepen their own math. Just as when googling, users can go where they need to, when they want to. The video clips come only from exemplary classrooms and commentary and analyses are provided by me and Maarten Dolk. In a very real sense, we are working alongside teachers and coaches (albeit in cyberspace) as they work to transform their teaching.

Coaches and consultants in districts using the platform have PLC portals on the platform to run local professional learning communities. When coaches set up their groups, the system makes members' responses in the notepads as they study the clips available to each other. This function allows the coach to gather information on which clips the community members have studied, what they noticed as they studied a lesson, what they believe is important in the teaching of that lesson, assessments they have made about what kids know, or don't know—all important information to inform the planning of activities and discussions when the PLC group convenes. College professors can use the platform and give assignments which make use of a rich library of video of young mathematicians at work and teachers hard at work mentoring—making the moments matter.

The idea is not to replace consultants and coaches, but to provide them with tools to make their work more powerful. For a long time we have talked about a "blended learning" approach to our programs for children, yet we often still use an archaic approach with teachers by making them wait for a coach or consultant's visit or a PD session, when answers to their questions are available immediately via the internet. P2S2™ provides for the use of a blended learning approach.

Some Closing Remarks

When Vygotsky wrote about the zone of proximal development, he was referring to what

---

[7] At the writing of this book 8 CFLM units are available at each grade, with more becoming available. Many districts I am working with are putting CFLM with **www.DreamBox.com** and achieving a core without the need of a textbook.[7]

a learner could do when working with a more knowledgeable other. I've always been a strong believer in the use of the terminology "co-teaching," instead of coaching. The latter has a connotation of a power hierarchy. Co-teaching is more akin with Vygotsky's notions of learning in the zone of proximal development and the role of dialogue.

Whenever I start working with a teacher in the classroom who is using my units, I always begin by telling the teacher that we will work together as a team. I lay down the rules of our work together. I won't do demos, and I will also never sit in the back of the room and then give feedback afterwards. Instead, I will co-teach and work as hard as I can to make each math workshop the best it can be. I will never hold back in sharing what I know about math development, what I anticipate the children will do with the investigations and why I and my team of writers crafted the contexts the way we did.

I ask the teacher for a similar commitment. The teacher knows more about the children, the families, and the school culture—far more than I can know by only just being invited to the classroom. Then we begin our work together. Once the teacher and I are working well as a team, we open the door to others in a professional learning community using P2S2, and fishbowl our work in the classroom with lesson studies as a focus of discussion and reflection. I invite administrators to be part of the process, too, and offer materials to parents[8]. It is crucial to realize that we are working in a system, not just with individuals and that we are living and working in a digital age.

As Peter Senge says in *The Fifth Dimension*, "Organizations change when their members can identify their most deeply ingrained assumptions, then unearth a shared picture of the future and go after it together." My hope is that our "shared picture" will focus on seeing beauty in children's mathematical ideas, strategies, and ways of modeling, and that teachers will be trusted to learn and provided with the needed opportunities to do so; that we come to understand the importance of mentoring the young mathematicians in our care and learn to question and confer in powerful ways that celebrate children's attempts and provide rich challenges to foster growth and development; and that we harness digital technologies to help us. And then, that we all go after this "shared picture" together.

---

[8] Our parent materials are now available in both Spanish and English and the next version of our online support system will include a parent portal.

REFERENCES

Ammon, P.A., & Levin, B.B. 1993. Expertise in teaching from a developmental perspective: The Developmental Teacher Education program at Berkeley. Learning and Individual Differences, 5 (4), 319326.

Anderson, C. 2000. *So How is it Going?* Portsmouth NH: Heinemann.

Anglin, W.S.. 1992. "Mathematics and History." *Mathematical Intelligencer*, Vol. 14, No. 4, pp. 6-12.

Beishuizen, M. 1993. Mental strategies and materials or models for addition and subtraction up to 100 in Dutch second grades. *Journal for Research in Mathematics Education*, 24, 294-323.

Bloom, B.S., Hastings, J. T. and Madaus, G. F. 1971. *Handbook on Formative and Summative Evaluation of Student Learning.* New York: McGraw-Hill.

Booth, J. 2005, April. Development and relations of different types of numerical estimation. Paper presented at the meeting of the Society for Research in Child Development in Atlanta, GA.

Booth, J. & Siegler, R. S. 2006. Numerical Magnitude Representations Influence Arithmetic Learning. **http://www.psy.cmu.edu/~siegler/boothsieginpress.pdf.**

Calkins, L. 1994. The Art of Teaching Writing. Portsmouth, NH: Heinemann.

Carey, S. 2009. Where our number concepts come from. *Journal of Philosophy, 106 (4)*, 220-254.

Carpenter, T. P.; Fennema, E.; Franke, M.; Levi, L.; Empson, S.B. 1999. *Children's Mathematics: Cognitively Guided Instruction.* Portsmouth, NH: Heinemann.

Confrey, J., Maloney, A., Nguyen, K., Mojica, G., & Myers, M. 2009. Equipartitioning/splitting as a foundation of rational number reasoning using learning trajectories. Paper presented at the 33rd Conference of the International Group for the Psychology of Mathematics Education, Thessaloniki, Greece.

Dehaene, S. 1997. *The Number Sense.* New York: Oxford University Press, 1997; Cambridge (UK): Penguin Press.

De Lange, J. 1992. Critical Factors for Real Changes in Mathematics Learning. pgs. 305-329 In *Assessment and Learning of Mathematics,* edited by G.C. Leder. Hawthorn, Victoria: Australian Council for Educational Research.

Devlin, K. 2003. *The Millennium Problems: The Greatest Unsolved Mathematical Puzzles of Our Time.* Cambridge, MA: Perseus.

Dweck, C. 2007. *Mindset: The New Psychology of Success.* New York: Random House.

Fosnot, C.T. and Dolk, M. 2001. *Young Mathematicians at Work: Constructing Early Number Sense, Addition and Subtraction.* Portsmouth NH: Heinemann.

Fosnot, C. T. and Dolk, M. 2002. *Young Mathematicians at Work: Constructing Fractions,* Portsmouth NH: Heinemann.

Fosnot, C.T. and Jacob, B. 2006. *Young Mathematicians at Work: Constructing Algebra.* Portsmouth NH: Heinemann.

Fosnot, C.T. and Jacob, B. 2009. Young Mathematicians at Work: The Role of Contexts and Models in the Emergence of Proof. In D. Stylianou, M. Blanton, and E. Knuth (Eds.). *Teaching and Learning Proof Across the Grades.* New York: Routledge.

Gagne, R. 1965. *The Conditions of Learning.* London: Holt, Rinehart, and Winston.

Gravemeijer, K. 1991. An instruction-theoretical reflection on the use of manipulatives. In *Realistic Mathematics Education in Primary School,* ed. Leen Streefland. Utrecht, The Netherlands: Freudenthal Institute.

Gravemeijer, K. 1999. How emergent models may foster the constitution of formal mathematics. *Mathematical Thinking and Learning,* 1(2), 155-77.

Klein, A.S.; Beishuizen, M.; and Treffers, A. 2002. The empty number line in Dutch second grade, In *Lessons Learned from Research,* eds. Judith Sowder and Bonnie Shapelle. Reston, VA. National Council of Teachers of Mathematics.

Krantz, S 2007. *The History and Concept of Mathematical Proof.* **http://www.eolss.net/Sample-Chapters/C02/E6-132-37.pdf.**

Moss, J. and Case, R., 1999. Developing Children's Understanding of the Rational Numbers: A New Model and an Experimental Curriculum. *Journal for Research in Mathematics Education*, Vol. 30, No. 2, 122–147.

Piaget, J. 1970. *Piaget's Theory.* NY: Wiley.

Ramani, G. B. & Siegler, R. S. 2008. Promoting Broad and Stable Improvements in Low-Income Children's Numerical Knowledge through Playing Number Board Games. *Child Development*, March/April 2008, Volume 79, Number 2, Pages 375–394.

Senge, P. 2006. *The Fifth Dimension: The Art & Practice of The Learning Organization.* NY: Doubleday.

Siegler, R. & Booth, J. 2004. Development of Numerical Estimation in Young Children. *Child Development.* March/April. Volume 75 (2). 428-444.

Steen, L. 1990. *On the Shoulders of Giants: New Approaches to Numeracy.* National Research Council.

Streefland, L. 1991. *Fractions in Realistic Mathematics Education: A Paradigm of Developmental Research.* Dordrecht: Kluwer.

Stylianou, D.; Blanton, M.; and Knuth, E. 2009. *Teaching and Learning Proof Across the Grades.* Studies in Mathematical Thinking and Learning Series. New York: Routledge.

van den Heuvel-Panhuizen, M. 1996. *Assessment and Realistic Mathematics Education.* Series on Research in Education, no. 19 (CD-B Press). Utrecht, The Netherlands, Utrecht University.

van den Heuvel-Panhuizen, M. and Fosnot, C.T. 2001. Not Only the Answers Count. *Proceedings of the 25th Conference of the International Group for the Psychology of Mathematics Education* (Volume 4, pp. 335-342). Utrecht: Freudenthal Institute, Utrecht University.

Vygotsky, L. 1978. *Mind in Society.* Cambridge, MA: Harvard University Press.

Wiles, A. 2000. On Solving Fermat's Last Theorem. November 1. NOVA **http://www.pbs.org/wgbh/nova/physics/andrew-wiles-fermat.html**

Made in the USA
Middletown, DE
01 May 2022

64927974R00077